Contents

Encourage Your Child to Develop a Growth Mindset

The research of psychologist Dr. Carol Dweck tells us that people have two possible mindsets—a fixed mindset or a growth mindset. People with a fixed mindset believe that they are either smart or good at something, or they are not—and nothing can change that. People with a growth mindset believe that it is always possible to get better at doing something. Dr. Dweck has found that students with a growth mindset are more motivated to learn and achieve more than students with a fixed mindset.

How can you help your child develop a growth mindset?

Talk about the brain. Explain that the brain becomes stronger by working hard to master new skills. Just as exercise makes muscles stronger, working at challenging thinking tasks makes the brain stronger.

View mistakes as learning opportunities. Let your child know that mistakes are valuable ways of learning where the problems lie. By carefully looking at mistakes, you and your child can learn where there are misunderstandings or missing pieces of knowledge. Mistakes pave the way to success!

Teach ways of dealing with frustration. Children can "turn off" when they become frustrated, which makes learning impossible. Teach your child ways to overcome frustration. For example, use the Internet to learn about breathing techniques that combat stress. You can also remind your child of skills that he or she mastered in the past (such as learning to tie shoelaces) that took time and effort to learn.

Focus on praising the process. While it's fine to praise your child or the results he or she achieved, you can encourage a growth mindset by focusing your praise on the process. For example, praise your child's willingness to keep trying and his or her use of effective learning strategies, such as asking questions.

Model a growth mindset. Look for opportunities to reinforce with your child how to see things from a growth mindset. For example:

If your child says…	Respond by saying…
I'll never get this!	Maybe you can't do it yet, but you'll get better if you keep trying.
I've been working at this for a long time and I'm still not getting it right.	Look at these areas where you've made progress. Keep working and you'll make more progress.
Hey, I can finally do this!	Let's think about how you achieved success. Some of the things you did this time might help you with the next challenge.

MONDAY • Sentences and Punctuation

1. A sentence tells a complete idea. *I drew a picture of two horses.*

Fill in the circle if the words make a sentence.

a) ◯ An old woman and a little girl.   **b)** ◯ The music is too loud.

2. The subject of a sentence tells who or what the sentence is about. <u>The whale</u> *swims away.*

Underline the subject in each sentence.

a) A toad jumps into the pond.   **b)** Clouds move across the sky.

3. Write the sentence. Correct the mistakes.

the sky is full of stars

_____

TUESDAY • Grammar and Usage

1. A noun names a person, place, or thing. *friend   schoolyard   button*

**Circle the people in red. Circle the places in blue.
Circle the things in green.**

school   mother   bike   town   John   toy   table   doctor

2. Write the correct word or words.

Linda's hair is _____ than Pat's hair.
　　　　　　　　　　longer　　　　the longest

**3. A plural noun names more than one person, place, or thing.
Make the nouns plural by adding *s*.**

a) cat: _____   **b)** book: _____   **c)** game: _____

WEDNESDAY • Vocabulary and Figurative Language

1. A <u>hole</u> is something you dig in the ground.
   <u>**Whole**</u> means "all of something."

   Write the correct word—*hole* or *whole*.

   Samantha ate the _____ muffin.

2. **Synonyms are words that have the same meaning.** *big – large*
   Circle the synonym for the bold word in the sentence.

   The race will **start** soon.   **end   begin   win**

3. **Find the mystery word that answers <u>both</u> riddles.**

   • You put me on a finger.
   • This is what you do to a doorbell.   **Mystery word: r ____ ____ ____**

THURSDAY • Phonics, Spelling, and Word Skills

1. **Answer the riddle with a word that has the long *a* sound.**

   This is what hockey players do.   s k ____ ____ ____

2. **A contraction is a short form of two words.** *do not   don't*
   An apostrophe (') takes the place of the letters that are left out.
   Write the correct contraction for each set of words.

   a) is not: _____   **b)** can not: _____   **c)** will not: _____

3. **A compound word is made of two smaller words.** *lady + bug = ladybug*
   Make two compound words from the words below.

   sun   ship   set   space

   _____

FRIDAY • Writing Prompts

Pretend you are 100 years old!
Draw a picture of what you will look like.

Where will you live?

_____

_____

How will you spend your time?

_____

_____

Here are some interesting facts about me when I am 100 years old:

_____

_____

_____

_____

- ☐ **My writing makes sense.**
- ☐ **I used capital letters where needed.**
- ☐ **I put the correct mark at the end of each sentence.**
- ☐ **My picture is neat and colourful.**

MONDAY • Sentences and Punctuation

1. **A sentence tells a complete idea.**   *Two birds sing in the tree.*

   Fill in the circle if the words make a sentence.

   a) ◯ The cat jumps on the chair.   **b)** ◯ The little boy fell down.

2. **A statement is a telling sentence. It ends with a (.)**
   A question is an asking sentence. It ends with a (?)
   Put the correct punctuation mark at the end of each sentence.

   a) I like baseball____   **b)** Can you come over____

3. **A command tells someone to do something. It ends with a (.) or an (!)**
   An exclamation shows a strong feeling. It ends with an (!).
   Put the correct end mark for each sentence.

   a) I love ice cream____   **b)** Come here____

TUESDAY • Grammar and Usage

1. **An adjective is a describing word.**   *a <u>tall</u> girl*   *the <u>funny</u> story*

   Underline the adjective in each group of words.

   a) an old house   **b)** the green sweater   **c)** a loud noise

2. **A verb is an action word. An action word tells what someone or something is doing. Write the correct verb.**

   I _____ computer games on rainy days.
       play   plays

3. **Write the correct word.**

   We cover our ears _____ the loud noise stops.
          after   until

 Canadian Daily Language Skills, Grade 2   © Chalkboard Publishing Inc.

WEDNESDAY • Vocabulary and Figurative Language

1. **A simile uses the words _like_ or _as_ to compare two things.**

   Finish the simile. Write the word below that makes sense.

   rocks   ice   fish

   The water in the lake is as cold as _____.

2. **Antonyms are words that have opposite meanings.** _big – small_
   Circle the antonym for the bold word.

   clean: tidy   wash   dirty

3. **Circle the meaning of the bold word in the sentence.**

   Gary let me use his red marker, and now I will **return** it.

   give back   take   turn around

THURSDAY • Phonics, Spelling, and Word Skills

1. **Answer the riddle. Use a word that ends with the letters _th_.**

   There are 12 of me in a year.   ____ ____ ____ t h

2. **Circle the words that have one syllable.**   today   step   big   after

3. **A base word (or root word) is a word that can be made into new words.**   _Base word: hard_   _New word: hard**er**_

   Write the base word.   _sleeping: sleep_

   a) watching: _____   **b)** played: _____

   c) swims: _____   **d)** taller: _____

FRIDAY • Writing Prompt

Draw a portrait of your family.

My family is special. Let me tell you why.

First of all, _____

_____

Another reason is _____

_____

Finally, _____

_____

This is why my family is special.

☐ **My writing makes sense.**
☐ **I used capital letters where needed.**
☐ **I put the correct mark at the end of each sentence.**
☐ **My picture is neat and colourful.**

MONDAY • Sentences and Punctuation

1. **A sentence tells a complete idea.** *I like playing computer games.*
   Fill in the circle if the words make a sentence.

   a) ◯ A large glass of milk.   **b)** ◯ The children like to run.

2. **The subject of a sentence tells who or what the sentence is about.**
   <u>A yellow kite</u> *flies in the sky.*

   Underline the subject in the sentence.   My uncle laughs at my jokes.

3. **Fill in the blank with the best joining word.**

   I waved at Sam, _____ he waved at me. (and   but)

4. **Put the correct punctuation mark at the end of each sentence.**

   a) What time is it____   **b)** I am so excited____

TUESDAY • Grammar and Usage

1. **When does the action happen—in the present or the past?**
   Circle the answer.

   a) Yesterday, we visited my grandmother.   **past   present**

   b) I see a rainbow in the sky.   **past   present**

2. **Use an apostrophe (') and *s* to show that something belongs to
   someone.**   *This book belongs to Kate. This is **Kate's** book.*
   Complete the sentence.

   This hat belongs to Nick. This is _____ hat.

3. **A plural noun names more than one person, place, or thing.**
   Add *es* to the nouns that end with *s, x, ch,* or *sh*.

   a) class_____   **b)** fox_____   **c)** lunch_____   **d)** dish_____

WEDNESDAY • Vocabulary and Figurative Language

1. People who are very kind have "a heart of gold."
I know Tom has a heart of gold because he always helps people.

Who do you think has a heart of gold? Tell why.

_____ has a heart of gold because

_____.

2. Synonyms are words that have the same meaning. *start – begin*
Circle the synonym for the bold word in the sentence.

The children played a **noisy** game outside.   **loud   fun   fast**

THURSDAY • Phonics, Spelling, and Word Skills

1. Answer the riddles with words that use the letters *ai* to make the long *a* sound.

a) You can find me on a cat, dog, or horse.   t ____ ____ ____

b) Water in a sink goes down me.   d r ____ ____ ____

2. Circle the base word of the bold word.

jumping: jum   jump   ping

3. A contraction is a short form of two words. *he is   he's*
An apostrophe (') takes the place of the letters that are left out.
Write the correct contraction for each set of words.

a) she is: _____   **b)** they are:_____   **c)** I am: _____

FRIDAY • Writing Prompt

Here is some advice. *You should treat people the way you want to be treated.*
Draw a picture.

I (agree disagree) with this advice. Let me tell you why.

First of all, _____

_____

Another reason is _____

_____

Finally, _____

_____

This is why I (agree disagree) with this advice.

☐ **My writing makes sense.**
☐ **I used capital letters where needed.**
☐ **I put the correct mark at the end of each sentence.**
☐ **My picture is neat and colourful.**

MONDAY • Sentences and Punctuation

1. A sentence tells a complete idea. *The clouds hide the sun.*

Fill in the circle if the words make a sentence.

a) ◯ Climbs up the tall ladder.　　**b)** ◯ The worm wiggles in the mud.

2. Who or what is the subject of the sentence? Underline the subject.

A blue butterfly flew in the window.

3. Fill in the blank with the best joining word.

I made a snack, _____ and I shared it with Tim.　　(and　but)

4. Put the correct punctuation mark at the end of each sentence.

a) I live in a city_____　　**b)** Put on your coat_____

TUESDAY • Grammar and Usage

**1. Proper nouns are words that name specific people or pets, places, holidays, days of the week, and months of the year.
Proper nouns begin with a capital letter.**

Sara　Orchard Mall　Christmas　Sunday　May

Write two examples of a proper noun.

_____

2. A pronoun takes the place of a noun. Look at the bold pronoun.

*The <u>boy</u> won the race. **He** is very happy.*

Write the missing pronoun.

A girl found my scarf. _____ gave it back to me.　　(he　she)

WEDNESDAY • Vocabulary and Figurative Language

1. **A simile uses the words *like* or *as* to compare two things.**

   Finish the simile. Write the word that makes sense.

   stone   leaf   tack

   The point on my pencil is as sharp as a _____.

2. **Circle the meaning of the bold word in the sentence.**
   Mom had a good **idea** for what to get Dad for his birthday.

    a thought   a question   a card

3. **Antonyms are words that have opposite meanings.** *clean – dirty*
   Circle the antonym for the bold word.

   first: beginning   middle   last

THURSDAY • Phonics, Spelling, and Word Skills

1. **Answer the riddles. Use words that begin with the letters *wh*.**

   a) I am a very big animal in the sea.   w h ____ ____ ____

   b) I turn around and around on a bike.   w h ____ ____ ____

2. **Circle the words that have two syllables.**

   funny   scrap   glass   under

3. **A compound word is made of two smaller words.**
   space + ship = spaceship

   Make two compound words from the words below.

   some   side   times   in

   _____

FRIDAY • Writing Prompt

- Facts are pieces of information that can be proven to be true.
- Opinions are views or beliefs a person has.

Choose a topic and fill in the table.

_____

Information	Fact or Opinion?	How do you know?

MONDAY • Sentences and Punctuation

1. Add words to make a complete sentence.

The little kitten _____.

2. Who or what is the subject in the sentence? Underline the subject.

a) The baseball player swings the bat.

b) A strong wind makes the trees bend.

3. Put the correct punctuation mark at the end of each sentence.

a) Call the police_____   **b)** Where are my shoes_____

TUESDAY • Grammar and Usage

1. An adjective describes a noun.   *a long rope*   *the bright light*

Circle the adjectives in each sentence.

a) The playful puppy chases a yellow butterfly.

b) Ellen gave me a gift in a tiny red box.

2. Write the correct word.

This building is the _____ building in our city.
taller   tallest

3. Write the correct word.

Everything looks white _____ it snows.
after   until

WEDNESDAY • Vocabulary and Figurative Language

1. _There_ is a place. *The book is <u>there</u>, on the table.*
   Their tells us that something belongs to more than one person.
   The birds built <u>their</u> nest in that tree.

   Write the correct word—*there* or *their*.

   Gail and Bob take off _____ boots.

2. **Synonyms are words that have the same meaning.** *loud – quiet*
   Circle the synonym for the bold word in the sentence.

   The man was shouting because he was **mad**.   **sad   angry   loud**

3. **Find the mystery word that answers <u>both</u> riddles.**
   • A man wears me around his neck.
   • This is what you do to shoelaces.   **Mystery word: ____ ____ ____**

THURSDAY • Phonics, Spelling, and Word Skills

1. **Answer the riddle with the word that uses the letters *ay* to make the long *a* sound.**

   This is what you do with toys.   ____ ____ a y

2. **A prefix is one or more letters added to the beginning of a base word. The prefix <u>un</u> can mean "not."** *un + kind = unkind (not kind)*

   Fill in the circle if the bold word makes sense in the sentence.

   a) ○ Greg was **unkind** when he said mean things to me.

   b) ○ Maria says it is **unkind** to help people.

3. **Write two more words in the same word family as the bold word.**

   brain: chain _____   _____

WANTED!

Who or what?

_____

Last seen?

_____

_____

Description?

_____

_____

Wanted for?

_____

_____

Reward?

_____

MONDAY • Sentences and Punctuation

1. **The predicate of a sentence tells what the subject does or is. The subject is in bold. The predicate is underlined.**
   My brother <u>plays soccer</u>.   *The woman* <u>is a doctor</u>.

   Underline the predicate in each sentence.

   a) Rabbits hop across the grass.   **b)** My dog barks at cats.

2. **Use commas in a list of three or more people or things.**
   We are going to buy a saw, a hammer, and nails at the store.

   Add commas to the list in the sentence.

   Sami David and Julie went fishing last weekend.

TUESDAY • Grammar and Usage

1. **Verbs are action words. Write the correct verbs.**

   My sister _____ aloud, and I _____.
   read   reads   listen   listens

2. **When does the action happen—in the present or the past? Circle the answer.**

   We open the window wide.   **past   present**

3. **Use an apostrophe (') and *s* to show that something belongs to someone.**   *This cat belongs to Lee. This is* **Lee's** *cat.*

   Complete the sentence.

   This bike belongs to Peter. This is _____ bike.

WEDNESDAY • Vocabulary and Figurative Language

1. **A simile uses the words _like_ or _as_ to compare two things.**

   Finish the simile. Write the word that makes sense.

   elephant   ant   umbrella

   This big box of books is as heavy as an _____.

2. **Antonyms are words that have opposite meanings.** _awake – asleep_
   Circle the antonym for the bold word.

   loud: noisy   quiet   hear

3. **Circle the meaning of the bold word.**

   We packed our suitcases to **prepare** for our trip.

   get ready   **wait**   **begin**

THURSDAY • Phonics, Spelling, and Word Skills

1. **Answer the riddle. Use a word that begins with the letters _bl_.**

   a) I am the colour of night.   b l ____ ____ ____

2. **Circle the words that have two syllables.**

   spin   over   rain   into

3. **A base word (or root word) is a word that can be made into new words.**   **Base word:** _lock_   **New word:** _un<u>lock</u>_

   Write the base word for each word.   _repaint: paint_

   a) untie: _____   **b)** redo: _____

   c) incorrect: _____   **d)** unhappy: _____

FRIDAY • Writing Prompt

What is your favourite holiday? Draw a picture.

My favourite holiday is _____. Let me tell you why.

First of all, _____

_____

Another reason is _____

_____

Finally, _____

_____

This is why _____ is my favourite holiday.

☐ **My writing makes sense.**
☐ **I used capital letters where needed.**
☐ **I put the correct mark at the end of each sentence.**
☐ **My picture is neat and colourful.**

MONDAY • Sentences and Punctuation

1. **The predicate of a sentence tells what the subject does or is.**
   The subject is in bold. The predicate is underlined.
   The tall man <u>sings a song</u>.   *Tara* <u>is my best friend</u>.

   Underline the predicate in each sentence.

   a) The long road is very bumpy.   **b)** I play soccer.

2. **Fill in the blank with the best joining word.**

   Sara wants to draw, _____ I want to paint.   (and   but)

3. **Put the correct punctuation mark at the end of each sentence.**

   a) Would you like a drink_____   **b)** This is amazing_____

TUESDAY • Grammar and Usage

1. **A pronoun takes the place of a noun. Look at the bold pronoun.**
   *The <u>girls</u> went home. **They** are going to do their homework.*

   Write the missing pronoun.

   Some <u>birds</u> are at the birdfeeder. _____ must be hungry.

2. **Use *a* before a word that starts with a consonant.**   *a nut   a dog*
   Use *an* before a word that starts with a vowel.   *an umbrella*
   Write *a* or *an*.

   a) _____ apple   **b)** _____ boy   **c)** _____ lamp   **d)** _____ owl

3. **Circle the correct word.**

   Jim and Max, please help (themselves   yourselves) to another muffin.

WEDNESDAY • Vocabulary and Figurative Language

1. **We say that something is "a piece of cake" when it is easy to do.**
   Counting to ten is a piece of cake.

   Tell something that is easy for you to do.

   I think that _____ is a piece of cake.

2. **Synonyms are words that have the same meaning.** *mad – angry*
   Circle the synonym for the bold word in the sentence.

   We picked some **beautiful** flowers in the garden.   **pretty   big   bright**

3. **Circle the meaning of the bold word in the sentence.**

   Dad asked us to **remove** our muddy shoes when we go in the house.

   move to a new place   put on   take off

THURSDAY • Phonics, Spelling, and Word Skills

1. **Answer the riddle with a word that uses the letters *ee* to make the long *e* sound.**

   You use these to help you walk.   f _____ _____ _____

2. **Fill in the circle if the bold word makes sense in the sentence.**

   a) ◯ Lisa was **unhappy** when her team won the game.

   b) ◯ My dad was **unhappy** when he lost his watch.

3. **Make two compound words from the words below.**

   coat   walk   rain   side

Canadian Daily Language Skills, Grade 2   © Chalkboard Publishing Inc.

FRIDAY • Writing Prompt

You have been chosen to be principal of your school for a week. Draw a picture.

If I were principal for a week I would do these things:

First, _____

Then, _____

Next, _____

Finally, _____

_____

- ☐ **My writing makes sense.**
- ☐ **I used capital letters where needed.**
- ☐ **I put the correct mark at the end of each sentence.**
- ☐ **My picture is neat and colourful.**

MONDAY • Sentences and Punctuation

1. **The predicate of a sentence tells what the subject does or is. The subject is in bold. The predicate is underlined.**
   The school bell <u>rang loudly</u>.   *The big box* <u>is heavy</u>.

   Underline the predicate in each sentence.

   a) The fire burns brightly.   **b)** The children are laughing.

2. **Fill in the blank with the best joining word.**

   Zebras have stripes, _____ they can run fast.   (and   but)

3. **Put the correct punctuation mark at the end of each sentence.**

   a) Today is Monday_____   **b)** Go to sleep_____

TUESDAY • Grammar and Usage

1. **A noun names a person, place, or thing.**   *Greg   forest   pencil*
   A verb can tell what someone or something does.   *swim   jump*

   Circle the nouns. Underline the verbs.

   speak   hop   soup   doctor   sandbox   stir

2. **Make the nouns plural. Hint: These nouns change their spelling.**

   a) mouse _____   **b)** person _____

   c) child _____   **d)** woman _____

3. **Write the correct pronoun.**

   Rick likes jokes, so I told _____ a very funny joke.   (he   him)

Canadian Daily Language Skills, Grade 2   © Chalkboard Publishing Inc.

WEDNESDAY • Vocabulary and Figurative Language

1. **A simile uses the words _like_ or _as_ to compare two things. Finish the simile. Write the word that makes sense.**

   butterfly   bird   fish

   Jill is a good swimmer. She swims like a _____.

2. **Find the mystery word that answers <u>both</u> riddles.**
   • There are lots of me in the alphabet.
   • You might get me in the mail.

   Mystery word: L ____ ____ ____ ____ ____ ____

3. **Circle the meaning of the bold word.**

   Your nose is in the **centre** of your face.   **outside   middle   inside**

THURSDAY • Phonics, Spelling, and Word Skills

1. **Answer the riddle. Use a word that begins with the letters _ch_.**

   I am a good place for you to sit.   c h ____ ____ ____

2. **Circle the words that have two syllables.**

   shark   tiger   sheep   robin

3. **The prefix _re_ means "again."** _re + read = reread (read again)_
   Fill in the circle if the bold word makes sense in the sentence.

   a) ◯ I love this story, so I **reread** it often.

   b) ◯ I don't like this book, so I will **reread** it.

4. **Write the correct contraction for each set of words.**

   a) he will: _____   **b)** they will:_____   **c)** I will: _____

FRIDAY • Writing Prompt

Draw someone or something that has gone missing. Complete the poster.

MISSING

Who or what: _____

When last seen: _____

Where last seen: _____

Description: _____

_____

If found, contact me at:

Reward

_____

MONDAY • Sentences and Punctuation

1. Put the correct punctuation mark at the end of each sentence.

  a) Who is knocking at the door_____   **b)** Two birds sit on a branch_____

2. Underline the predicate in the sentence.

  Mr. Sanchez is my brother's teacher.

3. Fill in the blank with the best joining word.

  I want to run, _____ my foot hurts.   (and   but)

4. Add commas to the list in the sentence as needed.

  I need a pencil eraser and paper to do my work.

TUESDAY • Grammar and Usage

1. An adjective describes a noun.   *a dark cloud*   *the cold water*

  Circle the adjectives in the sentence.

  The white rabbit has soft fur.

2. Write the correct word or words.

  The red car is _____ than the blue car.
                 faster   the fastest

3. When does the action happen—in the present or the future?

  a) We listen to the sound of the thunder.   **present future**

  b) The bird will fly back to its nest.   **present future**

WEDNESDAY • Vocabulary and Figurative Language

1. **A _tail_ is what some animals have.** *The dog wagged its tail.*
   A _tale_ is a story. *The teacher will read us a tale about a dragon.*

   Write the correct word—*tail* or *tale*.

   Dad told us a funny _____ about catching a fish.

2. **Circle the synonym for the bold word in the sentence.**

   The little boy was **scared** of the big dog.   **afraid   happy   sad**

3. **Circle the meaning of the bold word in the sentence.**

   I did not hear the question, so I asked the teacher to **repeat** it.

   answer   write   say again

THURSDAY • Phonics, Spelling, and Word Skills

1. **Answer the riddles with words that use the letters *ea* to make the long e sound.**

   a) This is what you do with a book.   ____ e a ____

   b) I grow on a tree or bush.   ____ e a ____

   c) I come out of a hot pot or kettle.   ____ ____ e a ____

2. **The prefix _dis_ means "not."** *dis + like = dislike (not like)*
   Fill in the circle if the bold word makes sense in the sentence.

   a) ○ I ate five meatballs because I **dislike** them.

   b) ○ I will not watch this movie again because I **dislike** it.

FRIDAY • Writing Prompt

A diamante poem is in the shape of a diamond.
Write your own diamante poem using the format below.

Topic _____

_____
(noun)

_____   _____
(adjective)   (adjective)

_____   _____   _____
("ing" verb)   ("ing" verb)   ("ing" verb)

_____   _____
(adjective)   (adjective)

_____
(noun)

MONDAY • Sentences and Punctuation

1. Put the correct end mark for each sentence.

a) Today is Anna's birthday_____

b) When is your birthday_____

2. Combine the two subjects to make one sentence.
Ken likes drawing. *Stacy* likes drawing.   *Ken and Stacy* like drawing.

The boy sings a song. The girl sings a song.

_____

3. Write the sentence. Correct the mistakes.

karen and i love riddles   _____

TUESDAY • Grammar and Usage

1. A pronoun can take the place of more than one noun.
Jack and *Paul* play together. **They** are friends.

Write the missing pronoun.

The rose and the tulip are red. _____ are very pretty.

2. Write the correct verbs.

Do birds _____ after the sun _____ down?
          fly   flies   go   goes

3. Circle the correct word in brackets.

You sit in your chair, and I'll sit in (my mine).

WEDNESDAY • Vocabulary and Figurative Language

1. **Finish the simile. Use the word that makes sense.**

   flower   rock   bee

   I don't like my new bed. It is as hard as a _____.

2. **Antonyms are words that have opposite meanings.** *loud – quiet*

   Circle the antonym for the bold word.

   closed: shut   moved   opened

3. **Circle the meaning of the bold word.**

   The firefighters **rescue** the cat from the burning house.

   save from danger   run away from   look for

THURSDAY • Phonics, Spelling, and Word Skills

1. **Answer the riddles. Use words that end with the letters** *ch***.**

   a) I am the name of a month.   ____ ____ ____ c h

   b) I am part of a tree.   ____ ____ ____ ____ c h

2. **Fill in the blank with the correct word.**

   I have _____ pieces of gum.   (two to)

3. **Correct and rewrite the sentence.**

   john made three wishs.

   _____

FRIDAY • Writing Prompt

Book Review

Book Title _____

Author _____

Genre _____

My Rating

☆ ☆ ☆ ☆ ☆

What was the book about? _____

_____

_____

Do you think other people would like the book? Explain your thinking.

_____

_____

_____

_____

☐ My writing makes sense.
☐ I used capital letters where needed.
☐ I put the correct mark at the end of each sentence.

MONDAY • Sentences and Punctuation

1. Put the correct punctuation mark at the end of each sentence.

a) You really scared me_____

b) Put your toys away_____

2. Who or what is the subject of this sentence? Underline the subject.

My green socks are nice and warm.

3. Choose the best word (*and* or *but*) to join the sentences. Remember to add a comma before the joining word.

The flowers are pretty. They smell nice.

_____

TUESDAY • Grammar and Usage

1. Write the plural of each noun.

a) bush: _____ **b)** peach: _____ **c)** ear: _____

2. When does the action happen—in the present or the future?

a) We will build a sandcastle in the sandbox. **present** **future**

b) The dogs bark at the squirrel. **present** **future**

3. Circle the adjectives in the sentence.

The furry kitten plays with a red ball.

WEDNESDAY • Vocabulary and Figurative Language

1. Someone who is very happy is "on cloud nine."
Jan was on cloud nine when she won the race.

Tell something that makes you feel like you are "on cloud nine."

I am on cloud nine when _____.

2. Circle the synonym for the bold word in the sentence.

Jamal worked hard to make his room **neat**.　　　**messy　　tidy　　happy**

3. Find the mystery word that answers <u>both</u> riddles.
• You see lots of me in a lake on a windy day.
• A person does this when saying "goodbye."

Mystery word: w _____ _____ _____ _____

THURSDAY • Phonics, Spelling, and Word Skills

1. Answer the riddle with a word that has the long *i* sound.

You do this with your teeth.　　　　　b _____ _____ _____

2. A suffix is one or more letters added to the end of a base word (or root word). We use the suffix <u>ing</u> with verbs.
*play + ing = playing　　　The children are **playing** in the sandbox.*

Write each verb. Add the suffix <u>ing</u>.

a) walk: _____　　**b)** read: _____

3. Write two more words in the same word family as the bold word.

grin: fin _____

FRIDAY • Writing Prompt

Write the steps for brushing your teeth.

First, _____

_____

_____

Next, _____

_____

_____

Then, _____

_____

_____

Finally, _____

_____

_____

MONDAY • Sentences and Punctuation

1. **Put the correct punctuation mark at the end of each sentence.**

   a) Take the dog for a walk_____   **b)** I love that joke_____

2. **When you write a date, use a comma after the day of the week and the number of the day.** *Thursday, April 16, 2020*

   Write today's date.

   _____

3. **Write an exclamation sentence about something you are excited about.**

   _____

TUESDAY • Grammar and Usage

1. **Circle the nouns. Underline the verbs.**

   road   mountain   write   think   dog   dig

2. **Write the correct verb.**

   I _____ this book, and it _____ great pictures.
       like   likes   has   have

3. **Write the correct word.**

   My sister likes reading books _____ this author.
                                        from   by

WEDNESDAY • Vocabulary and Figurative Language

1. **Finish the simile. Write the word that makes sense.**

   snow   water   sand   My new shirt is as white as _____.

2. **Find the mystery word that answers <u>both</u> riddles.**
   • I can help you see when it is dark.
   • I am a word for something that is not heavy.

   Mystery word: L ____ ____ ____ ____

3. **Circle the meaning of the bold word in the sentence.**

   Sarah had a **grin** on her face after she read the joke.

   mouth   bug   smile

THURSDAY • Phonics, Spelling, and Word Skills

1. **Answer the riddle. Use a word that begins with the letters *th*.**

   This is how you feel when you need water.   t h ___ ___ ___ ___ ___

2. **Circle the compound words.**

   into   over   under   maybe

3. **Remember to write *i* before *e* in these words: *piece   friend*.
   Use the clue to write the correct word.**

   a) This is a part of something. _____

   b) This is a person you like. _____

FRIDAY • Writing Prompt

Draw and label an invention that can help you with your daily life.

My invention is called _____

Let me tell you about how my invention helps me.

First of all, _____

_____

Another reason is _____

_____

Finally, _____

_____

This is how my invention helps me.

- ☐ **My writing makes sense.**
- ☐ **I used capital letters where needed.**
- ☐ **I put the correct mark at the end of each sentence.**
- ☐ **My picture is neat and colourful.**

MONDAY • Sentences and Punctuation

1. Add words to make a complete sentence.

_____ at the zoo.

2. Underline the subject in each sentence.

a) Rain falls all night long.

b) Two little mice run under the table.

3. Combine the two subjects to make one sentence.
A bird sits in the tree. _A squirrel_ sits in the tree.
A bird and a squirrel sit in the tree.

Jeff eats grapes. Kim eats grapes.

_____

TUESDAY • Grammar and Usage

1. An adverb can describe a verb. An adverb can tell <u>how</u> an action happens. _The sun shines <u>brightly</u>._   _Tina <u>carefully</u> opens the box._

Underline the adverb in the sentence.

Dad quietly closes the door.

2. Write the correct word.

A whale is the _____ animal in the sea.
bigger   biggest

3. Circle the correct word in brackets.

a) I found a mitten, and I think it is (your yours).

b) Shauna and Frank said, "Come and play with (me we us)!"

WEDNESDAY • Vocabulary and Figurative Language

1. **_Buy_ means "to pay for something."** *Dad will <u>buy</u> milk at the store.*
   _By_ can mean "near" or "close to." *We sat <u>by</u> a big apple tree.*

   Write the correct word—*buy* or *by*.

   You can _____ shoes at the store _____ the school.

2. **Circle the synonym for the bold word in the sentence.**

   Let's find a good **place** to sit in the sun.   **spot   house   warm**

3. **Circle the meaning of the bold word in the sentence.**

   I smell pine trees as soon as we **enter** the forest.

   go into   come out of   leave

THURSDAY • Phonics, Spelling, and Word Skills

1. **Answer the riddles with words that use *y* to make the long *i* sound.**

   a) Look up at me to see the moon.   ____ ____ y

   b) Babies do this when they are hungry.   ____ ____ y

   c) I am the month after June.   ____ ____ ____ y

2. **A suffix is one or more letters added to the end of a base word.**
   We use the suffix <u>ed</u> with some verbs to tell an action that happened
   in the past. *Yesterday, I open**ed** the window.*

   Write a verb with the suffix <u>ed</u>.

   Last night, I _____ a movie about a princess.

FRIDAY • Writing Prompt

Which do you like better, indoor recess or outdoor recess? Draw a picture.

I like _____ best. Let me tell you why.

First of all, _____

_____

Another reason is _____

_____

Finally, _____

_____

This is why I like _____ best!

☐ **My writing makes sense.**
☐ **I used capital letters where needed.**
☐ **I put the correct mark at the end of each sentence.**
☐ **My picture is neat and colourful.**

MONDAY • Sentences and Punctuation

1. Add words to make a complete sentence.

_____ in the sky.

2. Underline the predicate in the sentence.

A blue marble rolls across the floor.

3. Fill in the blank with the best joining word.

I thought I lost my pen, _____ I found it.   (and   but)

4. Correct and rewrite the sentence.

when is leo's birthday!

_____

TUESDAY • Grammar and Usage

1. Write the plural of each noun.

a) key: _____   **b)** baby: _____   **c)** box: _____

2. Write the correct verb.

Last week, we _____ some deer in the woods.
         see   saw

3. Circle the adjectives in the sentence.

Harry reads a funny book about a green turtle.

4. Circle the correct word in brackets.

The children get (ourselves   themselves) ready for bed.

WEDNESDAY • Vocabulary and Figurative Language

1. What do you think the underlined phrase means?
It started to rain during outdoor gym, so we <u>called it a day</u>.

_____

2. Write the sentence. Use the antonym of the bold word.
*The cookie jar is **empty**.*   *The cookie jar is <u>full</u>.*

It rained all **day**. _____.

3. Circle the meaning of the bold word in the sentence.

We get **rosy** cheeks when we play outside on a cold day.

pink   **warm**   **happy**

THURSDAY • Phonics, Spelling, and Word Skills

1. Answer the riddles. Use words that begin with the letters *sh*.

a) You can find me under a tree on a sunny day. s h ____ ____ ____

b) I am not a bath, but I will make you clean. s h ____ ____ ____ ____

c) I am a big fish with many sharp teeth. s h ____ ____ ____

2. Circle the words that have three syllables.

family   dinner   hospital   running   elephant

3. Circle the word that is the base word of the bold word.

a) speaks: speak   peak   pea   **b) refill:** ill   fill   ref

FRIDAY • Writing Prompt

Would you rather have warm weather or cold weather? Draw a picture.

I would rather have _____. Let me tell you why.

First of all, _____

_____

Another reason is _____

_____

Finally, _____

_____

This is why I would rather have _____.

☐ **My writing makes sense.**
☐ **I used capital letters where needed.**
☐ **I put the correct mark at the end of each sentence.**
☐ **My picture is neat and colourful.**

MONDAY • Sentences and Punctuation

1. Put the correct punctuation mark at the end of the sentence.

a) I see Mike over by the sandbox____   **b)** What is inside this box____

2. Combine the two predicates to make one sentence.
Amit is tall. *Amit has brown eyes*.   *Amit is tall and has brown eyes*.

The dog barked.   The dog jumped up.

_____

3. Underline the predicate in the sentence.

A big spider hangs in that web.

4. Write today's date as a sentence.

_____

TUESDAY • Grammar and Usage

1. An adverb can describe a verb. An adverb can tell how an action happens. *We sadly wave goodbye.*   *The dog barks angrily.*

Underline the adverb in the sentence.

The little baby laughs happily.

2. Write the correct verb.

The apples _____ red, and the banana _____ yellow.
　　　　　　　　is   are 　　　　　　　　　　　　is   are

3. Circle the correct word in brackets.

We saw (Wendys Wendy's) brother at the baseball game.

WEDNESDAY • Vocabulary and Figurative Language

1. Someone who is in trouble is "in hot water."
The bank robbers were <u>in hot water</u> when the police caught them.

What might you do that would get you "in hot water"?

I would be in hot water if I _____.

2. Circle the synonym for the bold word in the sentence.

My friend helps me feel better when I am **unhappy**.　　glad　　mad　　sad

3. Circle the meaning of the bold word in the sentence.

The house was **silent** when everyone was asleep.

very warm　　　**very noisy**　　　**very quiet**

THURSDAY • Phonics, Spelling, and Word Skills

1. Answer the riddles with words that use *i* to make the long *i* sound.

a) I am the person who makes an airplane fly.　　____ i ____ ____ ____

b) Use me to take wrinkles out of clothes.　　i ____ ____ ____

2. The prefix <u>re</u> means "again." *re + write = rewrite (write again)*
Fill in the circle if the bold word makes sense in the sentence.

a) ◯ The sentence has no mistakes, so I will **rewrite** it.

b) ◯ My printing is very messy, so I will **rewrite** the sentence.

3. Circle the compound words.

remember　　everyone　　surprise　　Sunday

FRIDAY • Writing Prompt

Write a letter to a friend.

_____
DATE

Dear _____,
GREETING

BODY

_____

_____

_____

_____

_____

_____

Your friend,

Checklist:

☐ **I included a greeting.**

☐ **My writing makes sense.**

_____
CLOSING / SIGNATURE

☐ **I checked for correct capitals and punctuation.**

☐ **I ended my letter with a closing and my name.**

MONDAY • Sentences and Punctuation

1. Put the correct punctuation mark at the end of the sentence.

a) How fast can sharks swim___   **b)** My birthday is in June___

2. Underline the predicate in the sentence. Circle the subject.

The carousel is in the park.

**3. Use the best word _(and_ or _or)_ to join the sentences.
Remember to add a comma.**

Everyone might leave. Some people might stay.

_____

TUESDAY • Grammar and Usage

1. Circle the nouns. Underline the verbs.

a) hide   straw   cloud   eat   zoo   bake

b) pillow   say   ant   take   think   desk

2. Complete the sentence.

Tomorrow, we _____ to see lions at the zoo.
                        go   will go

3. Write the correct word.

My new shoes are a gift _____ my Aunt Lucy.
                              by   from   for

WEDNESDAY • Vocabulary and Figurative Language

1. Finish the simile. Write the word that makes sense.

octopus   eagle   ant

If I had wings, I would fly like an _____.

2. Find the mystery word that answers both riddles.
• You look at me to tell the time.
• I am what you do at a movie.   **Mystery word:** w ____ ____ ____ ____

3. Write the sentence. Use the antonym of the bold word.
It rained all **day**.   *It rained all underlined{night}.*

She **remembers** to close the window.

_____

THURSDAY • Phonics, Spelling, and Word Skills

1. Answer the riddles. Use words that begin with the letters *sm*.

a) This is what noses can do.   sm ____ ____ ____

b) This is something your mouth can do.   sm ___ ___ ___

2. Each word has two syllables. Draw a line between the syllables.

a) r a i n b o w   **b)** i n t o   **c)** u n d e r

3. Remember that the vowels *e* and *a* go together when you spell these words: *early, ready*. Use the clue to write the correct word.

a) This word often comes after the word *get*. _____

b) This word is an antonym for *late*. _____

FRIDAY • Writing Prompt

An acrostic poem is a poem in which the first letters of each line spell out a word or phrase.

Print your name (vertically) down the left side.
Write an acrostic poem about yourself.

For example: **WALLY**

W hy
A m I
L ost in the
L ast snowstorm of the
Y ear

____ _____

____ _____

____ _____

____ _____

____ _____

____ _____

☐ **My writing makes sense.**
☐ **I used capital letters where needed.**
☐ **I put the correct mark at the end of each sentence.**

MONDAY • Sentences and Punctuation

1. Put the correct punctuation mark at the end of each sentence.

a) My new shoes are great___   **b)** My new shoes are blue ____

2. Combine the two predicates to make one sentence.

Maya _plays the piano_. Maya _sings_.   Maya _plays the piano and sings._

Some sharks are big. Some sharks have sharp teeth.

_____

3. Correct and rewrite the sentence.

when are you moving in june

_____

TUESDAY • Grammar and Usage

1. Write the correct word or words.

The big box is _____ than the small box.
                      heavier   the heaviest

2. Circle the plural nouns in the sentence.

The mice ran over the feet of some men and a woman.

3. Circle the correct word in brackets.

Kevin asks (myself himself) where he put his baseball glove.

4. Circle the nouns. Underline the verb.

The tall man takes a hammer from the bench.

WEDNESDAY • Vocabulary and Figurative Language

1. What do you think the underlined phrase means?
Mia let the <u>cat out of the bag</u>. Now everybody knows about the surprise!

_____

2. Ouch! Splash! Oink! These are "sound" words that sound like what they mean. When you use "sound" words, it is called *onomatopoeia*.

Circle the onomatopoeic word in the sentence.

The bacon sizzled in the pan.

3. Find the mystery word that answers <u>both</u> riddles.
• You find me on a tree.
• This is what dogs do.   **Mystery word:** b _____ _____ _____

THURSDAY • Phonics, Spelling, and Word Skills

1. Answer the riddle with a word that uses the letters *igh* to make the long *i* sound.

I am the antonym for the word *low*.   h _____ _____ _____

2. The prefix <u>*dis*</u> means "not." *dis + honest = dishonest (not honest)*

Fill in the circle if the bold word in the sentence makes sense.

a) ◯ It is **dishonest** to tell a lie.

b) ◯ Jamal never tells a lie, so he is **dishonest**.

3. Fill in the blank with the correct word.

Are you going _____ the party?   (to   two)

FRIDAY • Writing Prompt

Write about a special place you have visited.

_____ **is a special place. Let me tell you why.**

First of all, _____

_____

Another reason is _____

_____

Finally, _____

_____

This is why _____ is a special place.

☐ **My writing makes sense.**
☐ **I used capital letters where needed.**
☐ **I put the correct mark at the end of each sentence.**
☐ **My picture is neat and colourful.**

MONDAY • Sentences and Punctuation

1. Put the correct punctuation mark at the end of the sentence.

Close the window___

2. Underline the predicate in the sentence. Circle the subject.

Loud thunder scares the children.

3. Choose the best word (*and* or *or*) to join the sentences. Remember to add a comma.

Giraffes have long legs. They can run fast.

_____

TUESDAY • Grammar and Usage

1. Write the correct verb.

We all _____ loudly, but Jill _____ the loudest.
     sing   sings   sing   sings

2. Circle the correct word in brackets.

a) This dog does not belong to us. This dog is not (ours our).

b) Ali put (its his) hat on the table by the door.

3. Write the correct word.

The _____ toys are all on the bottom shelf.
    children's   childrens

WEDNESDAY • Vocabulary and Figurative Language

1. **Finish the simile. Write the word that makes sense.**

   diamonds   trees   clouds

   The shiny, silver shoes sparkle like _____.

2. **Write the sentence. Use the antonym of the bold word.**
   *This question is **easy**.   This question is <u>hard</u>.*

   Today, we have **less** homework.

   _____

3. **Circle the meaning of the bold word in the sentence.**

   The towel was **damp** after I used it to dry my hands.

   very dry   a little bit wet   cold

THURSDAY • Phonics, Spelling, and Word Skills

1. **Answer the riddles. Use words that end with the letters *sh*.**

   a) You might do this to someone on a swing.   ____ ____ s h

   b) I help make hair neat.   ____ ____ ____ s h

2. **Each word has two syllables. Draw a line between the syllables.**

   a) w i n t e r   **b)** n u m b e r   **c)** M o n d a y

3. **Use a word from below to complete the compound word.**

   blue   beach   sun   box

   a) _____flower   **b)** sand_____

FRIDAY • Writing Prompt

Write a postcard to a friend.

Front of Postcard:

Back of Postcard:

To:

MONDAY • Sentences and Punctuation

1. Put the correct punctuation mark at the end of each sentence.

a) Have you seen this movie before____

b) Tell Rick to wait for me____

2. Fill in the circle if the words make a complete sentence.

a) ◯ The bus is coming.

b) ◯ I hear someone singing.

3. Combine the two subjects to make one sentence.

A red bird is in the photo. A big dog is in the photo.

_____

TUESDAY • Grammar and Usage

1. An adverb can describe a verb. An adverb can tell <u>how</u> an action happens. *The sun shines <u>brightly</u>.* *Tina <u>carefully</u> opens the box.*

Underline the adverb in the sentence.

Mario gently holds the tiny kitten.

2. Write the correct verb.

Now I _____ seven years old.
       was   am   will be

3. Write the correct word.

My foot got wet when I stepped _____ a puddle.
                              on   into   over

WEDNESDAY • Vocabulary and Figurative Language

1. **Someone who is not feeling well is "under the weather."**
   Dad didn't go to work because he is <u>under the weather</u> today.

   Tell what you do—or don't do—when you are "under the weather."

   When I am under the weather, I _____

   _____.

2. **The word <u>our</u> tells who something belongs to.**
   These toys belong to my brother and me. They are <u>our</u> toys.
   An <u>hour</u> is an amount of time. *It takes one <u>hour</u> to drive to the lake.*

   Write the correct word—*our* or *hour*.

   The white house at the end of the street is _____ house.

THURSDAY • Phonics, Spelling, and Word Skills

1. **Answer the riddles with words that have the long *o* sound.**

   a) A scoop of ice cream sits on top of me.   c ____ ____ ____

   b) You see me when a fire is burning.   s m ____ ____ ____

2. **For each word, underline the base word and circle the prefix.**

   a) remake   **b)** disappear   **c)** untie

3. **Remember to write a *d* before the *g* in these words: *bridge, fudge*.**
   Use the clue to write the correct word.

   a) You can go over or under this.   _____

   b) This might stick to your teeth.   _____

FRIDAY • Writing Prompt

Write the steps for how to make something. Draw a picture of what you are making.

How to a make _____

What you need:

_____

What you do:

1. First, _____

2. Second, _____

3. Next, _____

4. Then, _____

5. Finally, _____

MONDAY • Sentences and Punctuation

1. What kind of sentence is it? Circle the answer.

a) Why do birds sing?   **statement   command   question**

b) The baby is so cute!   **command   exclamation   question**

2. Fill in the blank with the best joining word.

I could watch a movie, _____ it is almost my bedtime.
                                    and   but

3. Underline the predicate in the sentence. Circle the subject.

The boys rolled all the way down the hill.

TUESDAY • Grammar and Usage

1. Write *a* or *an* before each word.

a) _____ goat   **b)** _____ egg   **c)** _____ umbrella   **d)** _____ mall

2. Write the correct word or words.

A bee sting is _____ than a mosquito bite.
                        worse   the worst

3. Circle the correct word in brackets.

a) We should give (yourself   ourselves) more time to walk to school.

b) Two birds wash (itself   themselves) in our birdbath.

WEDNESDAY • Vocabulary and Figurative Language

1. **Finish the simile. Write the word that makes sense.**

   pancake   mountain   banana

   This road is as flat as a _____.

2. **Ouch! Splash! Oink! These are "sound" words that sound like what they mean. When you use "sound" words, it is called *onomatopoeia*.**

   What animal makes this sound?   **Moo!** _____

3. **Circle the meaning of the bold word in the sentence.**

   The questions on the test were **simple**, so I finished the test quickly.

   hard   long   easy

THURSDAY • Phonics, Spelling, and Word Skills

1. **Answer the riddles. Use words where the letters *ph* make the same sound as the letter *f*.**

   a) Use me to talk to someone far away.   p h ____ ____ ____

   b) You say me when you go from a to z.   ____ ____ p h____ ____ e t

2. **We use the suffix *er* in some words that tell what someone does.** *Mr. Chang will teach us. He is our teacher.*

   Complete the sentences. Use a word with the suffix *er*.

   a) My aunt has a farm. She is a _____.

   b) Mr. Costa loves to sing. He is a _____.

FRIDAY • Writing Prompt

A diamante poem is in the shape of a diamond.
Write your own diamante poem using the format below.

Topic _____

_____
(noun)

_____   _____
(adjective)   (adjective)

_____ _____ _____
("ing" verb)   ("ing" verb)   ("ing" verb)

_____   _____
(adjective)   (adjective)

_____
(noun)

MONDAY • Sentences and Punctuation

1. Put the correct punctuation mark at the end of each sentence.

a) I have two sisters and one brother____   **b)** I am so excited____

2. Combine the two predicates to make one sentence.

An airplane has wings. An airplane can fly far.

_____

3. Write the sentence. Correct the mistakes.

will you help frida do her homework

_____

TUESDAY • Grammar and Usage

1. Write the plural of each noun.

a) city: _____   **b)** monkey: _____

2. Write the correct verb.

Jamie always _____ at us when we _____ him.
         smile   smiles   see   sees

3. Circle the correct word.

a) Is this Paul's coat? I will ask if it is (him his).

b) Some geese make (its their) nests in tall grass.

WEDNESDAY • Vocabulary and Figurative Language

1. **_Right_ can mean "correct" or "the opposite of left."**
   Janet was <u>right</u> *when she said today is Tuesday.*
   I put my <u>right</u> *foot in front of my left foot.*

   Write is what you do when you put words on paper.
   I will <u>write</u> *a story about an elephant and a lion.*

   Write the correct word—*right* or *write*.

   I wonder if Max will _____ the _____ answer.

2. **Circle the meaning of the bold word in the sentence.**

   The thunder and lightning **frighten** the children.

   make afraid   make happy   make sad

THURSDAY • Phonics, Spelling, and Word Skills

1. **Answer the riddles with words that use the letters *oa* to make the long *o* sound.**

   a) Cars and trucks drive on me.   r ____ ____ ____

   b) I can take you on a trip across water.   b ____ ____ ____

2. **Use words from below to complete the two compound words.**

   drop   hammer   finger   shoe

   a) _____nail   **b)** rain_____

3. **Write two more words in the same word family as the bold word.**

   book: hook _____

FRIDAY • Writing Prompt

Design your own Canadian $1 coin.

 This is what a real $1 coin looks like!

CANADA

1988

DOLLAR

The nickname for the Canadian $1 coin is the loonie.
What is the nickname of your $1 coin, and why?

_____

_____

_____

☐ **My writing makes sense.**
☐ **I used capital letters where needed.**
☐ **I put the correct mark at the end of each sentence.**
☐ **My picture is neat and colourful.**

MONDAY • Sentences and Punctuation

1. **You can use _so_ or _because_ to join two sentences.**
   Put a comma before _so_. Do not put a comma before _because_.
   Use the best word (_so_ or _because_) to join the sentences.

   Jim is very tired. He will sleep well tonight.

   _____

2. **Add commas to the list in the sentence.**

   I like baseball hockey soccer and swimming.

3. **Write the sentence. Correct the mistakes.**

   can some snakes swim

   _____

TUESDAY • Grammar and Usage

1. **An <u>adjective</u> describes a noun. An <u>adverb</u> can describe a verb.**
   An adverb can tell <u>how</u> an action happens.

   Circle the adjective. Underline the adverb.

   a) My new friend softly whispers a secret.

   b) Cindy laughed loudly at the silly joke.

2. **Complete the sentence.**

   Last year, I _____ on a ride in a helicopter.
   go   went   will go

3. **Write the correct word.**

   We saw lots of trains _____ the train station.
   to   for   at

WEDNESDAY • Vocabulary and Figurative Language

1. Finish the simile. Write the word that makes sense.

horse   snake   giraffe

This tree is growing very tall. It is as tall as a _____.

2. Circle the meaning of the bold word in the sentence.

The farmer wakes up very early, and she starts working at **dawn**.

when the sun comes up   when the sun goes down   night

3. Write the sentence. Use the antonym of the bold word.

Pedro walked **over** the bridge.

_____

THURSDAY • Phonics, Spelling, and Word Skills

1. Answer the riddles. Use words that end with the letters *tch*.

a) You can do this to a ball.   ____ ____ t c h

b) I tell you the time.   ____ ____ t c h

c) You might do this when you have an itch.   ____ ____ ____ ____ t c h

2. Each word has two syllables. Draw a line between the syllables.

a) p e r f e c t   **b)** b a c k p a c k   **c)** s a d n e s s

**3. The prefix _re_ means "again." *re + heat = reheat (heat again)*
Fill in the circle if the bold word makes sense in the sentence.**

a) ◯ Mom put the hot pizza in the oven to **reheat** it.

b) ◯ The soup got cold, so Dad will **reheat** it.

FRIDAY • Writing Prompt

Book Review

Book Title _____

Author _____

My Rating

Genre _____ ☆☆☆☆☆

What was the book about? _____

_____

_____

Do you think other people would like the book? Explain your thinking.

_____

_____

_____

_____

☐ **My writing makes sense.**
☐ **I used capital letters where needed.**
☐ **I put the correct mark at the end of each sentence.**

 Canadian Daily Language Skills, Grade 2   © Chalkboard Publishing Inc.

MONDAY • Sentences and Punctuation

1. **What kind of sentence is it? Circle the answer.**

   a) The rain has stopped now.   **exclamation   command   statement**

   b) Take your shoes off.   **statement   command   question**

   c) I am very afraid!   **question   statement   exclamation**

2. **Add words to make a complete sentence.**

   My friend and I _____.

3. **Write a sentence that includes a list of your favourite snacks. Remember to add commas to the list in the sentence.**

   _____

TUESDAY • Grammar and Usage

1. **Circle the nouns and underline the verb in the sentence.**

   The elephants drink water from the pond.

2. **Write the correct word.**

   I think soccer is the _____ of all sports.
                             better   best

3. **Circle the correct word in brackets.**

   I see two girls. The (girls girl's girls') parents are talking to them.

4. **Write the correct word.**

   Kim used her towel to dry _____ after swimming.
                                    herself   itself

WEDNESDAY • Vocabulary and Figurative Language

1. Someone is "on top of the world" when they are very happy.
I am on top of the world because today is my birthday.

Tell about something that made you feel "on top of the world."

I was on top of the world when _____

_____.

2. Circle the synonym for the bold word in the sentence.

The car **nearly** ran into the bus.   **almost   always   never**

3. Find the mystery word that answers <u>both</u> riddles.
• I am what you do on a bed.
• I am something that is not true.   **Mystery word:** I ____ ____

THURSDAY • Phonics, Spelling, and Word Skills

1. Answer the riddles with words that use *ow* to make the long *o* sound.

a) I might fall from the sky on a cold day.   ____ ____ o w

b) You might put hot soup in me.   ____ o w ____

2. A prefix is one or more letters added to the beginning of a base word. The prefix <u>un</u> means "not." *un + fair = unfair (not fair)*

Fill in the circle if the bold word makes sense in the sentence.

a) ◯ It is **unfair** that Sandy always gets to go down the slide first.

b) ◯ It is **unfair** that each child gets one ride on the pony.

3. Write two more words in the same word family as the bold word.

straw: jaw _____

FRIDAY • Writing Prompt

**What kind of magic object or animal would you like to have?
Draw your magic object or animal.**

I would like to have a magic _____. Let me tell you why.

First of all, _____

_____

Another reason is _____

_____

Finally, _____

_____

This is why I would like to have a magic _____.

- [ ] **My writing makes sense.**
- [ ] **I used capital letters where needed.**
- [ ] **I put the correct mark at the end of each sentence.**
- [ ] **My picture is neat and colourful.**

MONDAY • Sentences and Punctuation

1. Put the correct punctuation mark at the end of each sentence.

   a) Be quiet when the baby is sleeping_____

   b) Hurray, our team won the game____

2. Add commas to the list in the sentence.

People made cakes cookies and muffins for the bake sale.

3. Underline the predicate in the sentence.

The monkeys played in the treetops.

4. What kind of sentence is it? Circle the answer.

Do you want to play soccer?   **command   exclamation   question**

TUESDAY • Grammar and Usage

1. Write the plural of each noun. Hint: The spelling changes.

   a) leaf: _____   **b)** tooth: _____

2. Circle the correct word in brackets.

I found my boots, but Dan and Anna are still looking for (theirs their).

3. Write the correct word.

This toy comes _____ two batteries.
                    with   from   in

4. Write the correct verb or verbs.

Next year, our dog _____ five years old.
                    was   is   will be

WEDNESDAY • Vocabulary and Figurative Language

1. Finish the simile. Write the word that makes sense.

trees   sugar   glass

The ice on the pond is as smooth as _____.

2. Circle the meaning of the bold word in the sentence.

Dad will **remind** me that I have homework to do tonight.

make someone remember   make someone forget   ask someone

3. Ouch! Splash! Oink! These are "sound" words that sound like what they mean. When you use "sound" words, it is called *onomatopoeia*.

What animal makes this sound?

a) Baa! _____   **b) Quack!** _____

THURSDAY • Phonics, Spelling, and Word Skills

1. Answer the riddles. Use words that end with the letters *dge*.

a) You see me on the chest of a police officer.   ____ ____ d g e

b) I am a sweet and chewy kind of candy.   ____ ____ d g e

c) I am a row of bushes growing close together.   ____ ____ d g e

2. Each word has three syllables. Draw a line between the syllables.

a) S e p t e m b e r   **b)** h a m b u r g e r

3. Use <u>one</u> of the words below to make <u>two</u> compound words.

under   over   out   be

a) with_____   **b)** _____side

FRIDAY • Writing Prompt

Complete the advertisment to sell a house. Draw the house.

Buy this _____ house!

Description

_____

_____

_____

_____

Selling Price _____ **Contact Number** _____

- ☐ My writing makes sense.
- ☐ I used capital letters where needed.
- ☐ I put the correct mark at the end of each sentence.
- ☐ My picture is neat and colourful.

MONDAY • Sentences and Punctuation

1. You can use _so_ or _because_ to join two sentences.

Put a comma before _so_. Do not put a comma before _because_.
Choose the best word (_so_ or _because_) to join the sentences.

I need to do my homework. It is almost bedtime.

_____

2. Add commas to the list in each sentence.

a) We got gum suckers apples and chocolate bars on Halloween.

b) I have yellow red orange and blue pencils in my knapsack.

TUESDAY • Grammar and Usage

1. An <u>adjective</u> describes a noun. An <u>adverb</u> can describe a verb.
An adverb can tell <u>how</u> an action happens.

Circle the adjective. Underline the adverb.

The children safely cross the busy street.

2. Write the correct verb.

Tara _____ a cat, and we _____ two dogs.
       has   have   has   have

3. Circle the correct word.

Robert made this birthday card by (itself himself).

WEDNESDAY • Vocabulary and Figurative Language

1. A _pear_ is a kind of fruit. _Linda was hungry, so she ate a pear._
   A _pair_ is two of something. _I will put on a warm pair of socks today._

   Write the correct word—_pear_ or _pair_.

   Dad cut up a _____ to eat with some yogurt.

2. **Circle the synonym for the bold word in the sentence.**

   Some fish are big, but whales are **enormous**.   **huge   small   fast**

3. **Circle the meaning of the bold word in the sentence.**

   Mom asked me not to **mention** the surprise party for Dad.

   talk about   remember   get ready for

THURSDAY • Phonics, Spelling, and Word Skills

1. **Answer the riddles with words that have the long _u_ sound.**

   a) I am a word that means "very big."   ____ u ____ ____

   b) To not get in trouble, follow these.   ____ u ____ ____ ____

2. **The prefix _dis_ means "not."** _dis + agree = disagree (not agree)_

   Fill in the circle if the bold word makes sense in the sentence.

   a) ◯ Jeff thinks hockey is the best sport, but I **disagree** because
       I love baseball.

   b) ◯ Lisa and I like all the same things, so we **disagree** often.

FRIDAY • Writing Prompt

Write a letter to convince your teacher that the class should have a day off school.

_____
DATE

Dear _____,
GREETING

BODY

_____

_____

_____

_____

_____

_____

Sincerely,

Checklist:

☐ I included a greeting.

☐ My writing makes sense.

_____
CLOSING / SIGNATURE

☐ I checked for correct capitals and punctuation.

☐ I ended my letter with my name.

MONDAY • Sentences and Punctuation

1. Put the correct punctuation mark at the end of the sentence.

a) Someone is at the door____

b) Are all these gifts for me____

2. Fill in the circle if the words make a complete sentence.

a) ◯ The hockey game has begun.

b) ◯ Running as fast as they can.

3. Combine the two predicates to make one sentence.

The snow is melting. The snow will soon be gone.

_____

TUESDAY • Grammar and Usage

1. Circle the nouns. Underline the verbs.

Noisy children run and play in the park.

2. Write the correct word.

This cold is the _____ cold I have ever had.
worse   worst

3. Complete each sentence with the correct verb.

a) Today, I _____ happy that the sun is shining.
am   is   was

b) Marco _____ with his friends yesterday morning.
play   plays   played

WEDNESDAY • Vocabulary and Figurative Language

1. **Finish the simile. Write the word that makes sense.**

   feather   rock   kitten

   The little caterpillar is as light as a _____.

2. **Ouch! Splash! Oink! These are "sound" words that sound like what they mean. When you use "sound" words, it is called *onomatopoeia*.**

   What makes this sound?

   a) Tick Tock! _____   **b) Woof!** _____

3. **Circle the meaning of the bold word in the sentence.**

   The robber ran to **escape** from the police.

   get away   go toward   come back

THURSDAY • Phonics, Spelling, and Word Skills

1. **Answer the riddle. Use a word that starts with the letters *scr*.**

   A mosquito bite makes you do this.   s c r ____ ____ ____ ____

2. **Each word has three syllables. Draw a line between the syllables.**

   a) w a t e r f a l l   **b)** b a r b e c u e

3. **The suffix _er_ can mean "more."**
   It is _more quiet_ in this room.   It is _quieter_ in this room.

   Write the sentence. Use the suffix _er_ instead of "more."

   The grass looks _more green_ now.

   _____

FRIDAY • Writing Prompt

What is a tradition in your family? Draw a picture.

A tradition in my family is _____.

Let me tell you about it. _____

_____

_____

_____

_____

- [ ] **My writing makes sense.**
- [ ] **I used capital letters where needed.**
- [ ] **I put the correct mark at the end of each sentence.**
- [ ] **My picture is neat and colourful.**

MONDAY • Sentences and Punctuation

1. What kind of sentence is it? Circle the answer.

a) The fire truck is red.   **statement   command   question**

b) Do you want to play outside? **command   exclamation   question**

c) Please stop doing that! **command   exclamation   question**

2. Use quotation marks at the beginning and end of the words that someone says.   *"It is nice to see you," said Mr. Adams.*

Add quotation marks to each sentence.

a) We will have fun, said Tara.

b) I like when it snows, said Lewis.

TUESDAY • Grammar and Usage

1. Underline the plural nouns in the sentence.

The people clap after the women sing two songs.

2. Circle the correct word in brackets.

a) I play soccer with (Tammy's Tammys) brother.

b) The girls saw two (animals animals') footprints in the snow.

3. Write the correct pronoun.

a) "Would you like to eat lunch with Emily and _____?" asked Tim.
                                                         I   me

b) My dad and _____ like to go for walks together.
                              I   me

WEDNESDAY • Vocabulary and Figurative Language

1. Something that happens "once in a blue moon" does not happen very often. *Mom lets me stay up late once in a blue moon.*

Tell something that happens "once in a blue moon."

_____ is

something that happens once in a blue moon.

2. Circle the synonym for the bold word in the sentence.

We need to **rush**, or we will be late.　　　**hurry　walk　stay**

3. Find the mystery word that answers the riddle.
• I am hard and you find me on the ground.

Mystery word: r ____ ____ k

THURSDAY • Phonics, Spelling, and Word Skills

1. Answer the riddles with words that use *ew* to make the long *u* sound.

a) I am the antonym for the word *old*.　　　____ e w

b) You do this when you eat.　　　____ ____ e w

c) I am like a nail, but you turn me in circles.　　　____ ____ ____ e w

2. Choose <u>one</u> of the words below to make <u>two</u> compound words.

hair　glue　paint　tooth

a) _____paste　　　**b)** _____brush

3. Circle the words made from a prefix and a base word.

reading　　　recount　　　rename　　　resting

FRIDAY • Writing Prompt

A proverb is a saying that gives wise advice.

For example: *Money doesn't grow on trees.*

Draw a picture of the proverb.

Do you think this is good advice? ☐ Yes ☐ No

Explain your thinking. _____

_____

Write your own saying to give advice about money.

Money _____

☐ **My writing makes sense.**
☐ **I used capital letters where needed.**
☐ **I put the correct mark at the end of each sentence.**
☐ **My picture is neat and colourful.**

MONDAY • Sentences and Punctuation

1. Underline the predicate in the sentence. Circle the subject.

Sandy and Tasneem played lacrosse in the park.

2. Use quotation marks at the beginning and end of words that someone says. *Mom asked, "How was school today?"*

Add quotation marks to each sentence.

a) Carlos asked, May I play, too?

b) Mia asked, are you in grade two?

3. Combine the two predicates to make one sentence.

The school is big. The school has lots of windows.

_____

TUESDAY • Grammar and Usage

1. Circle the adjective. Underline the adverb.

The knight bravely fights the huge dragon.

2. Write the correct verbs.

The girls _____ happy, but I _____ even happier.
              is   are   am   is

3. Write the correct word.

My hair got wet _____ I walked in the rain.
                as   after   until

4. Write a sentence tthat includes a noun that names a place.

_____

WEDNESDAY • Vocabulary and Figurative Language

1. **Finish the simile. Write the word that makes sense.**

   stars   night   thunder

   The huge bear was as black as _____.

2. **Write the sentence. Use the antonym of the bold word.**

   I had a nap **before** the soccer game.

   _____

3. **Circle the meaning of the bold word in the sentence.**

   The hungry mice **nibble** on a cookie that fell on the floor.

   play with   **run around**   **eat in small bites**

THURSDAY • Phonics, Spelling, and Word Skills

1. **Answer the riddles. Use words that start with the letters *spr*.**

   a) I am the name of a season.   s p r ____ ____ ____

   b) You do this to jam on toast.   s p r ____ ____ ____

2. **Circle the word that is the base word of the bold word.**

   a) uncover: over   cover   cove   **b) rewrite:** rite   re   write

3. **The suffix *est* means "most."**
   This light is the most bright.   *This light is the brightest.*

   Complete the sentence. Use a word with the suffix *est*.

   This juice is the most sweet.

   This juice is the _____.

FRIDAY • Writing Prompt

Write the recipe for a silly sandwich using unusual food combinations. Draw a picture of your sandwich.

Name Your Silly Sandwich

_____

Ingredients

_____ _____ _____

_____ _____ _____

Instructions

First, _____

Then, _____

Next, _____

After, _____

Finally, _____

- [ ] **My writing makes sense.**
- [ ] **I used capital letters where needed.**
- [ ] **I put the correct mark at the end of each sentence.**
- [ ] **My picture is neat and colourful.**

MONDAY • Sentences and Punctuation

1. Put the correct punctuation mark at the end of each sentence.

a) Walk quietly down the hall____

b) Do you play hockey on Saturdays____

2. Add commas to the list in each sentence.

a) The pet store sells kittens puppies fish and hamsters.

b) Birds raccoons and foxes live in the forest.

3. Write the sentence. Correct the mistakes.

What a nice surprise!" said Mom

_____

TUESDAY • Grammar and Usage

1. Circle the nouns. Underline the verb.

A bus and a truck drive down the bumpy road.

2. Write the correct word or words.

This little fly is _____ than a bee.
tinier   tiniest

3. Complete the sentence.

Next year, I _____ taller than I am this year.
am   will be   was

4. Circle the correct word.

The orange butterfly hid (himself itself) behind some leaves.

WEDNESDAY • Vocabulary and Figurative Language

1. **Circle the synonym for the bold word.**

   I made a **gift** for Dad for his birthday.   card   cake   **present**

2. **Circle the meaning of the bold word in the sentence.**

   I know I am very cold when my body starts to **shiver**.

   shake   sleep   get hungry

3. **Fill in the circle if the sentence has a simile.**

   a) ◯ The fire alarm was as loud as a siren.

   b) ◯ I like strawberry jam on toast.

   c) ◯ Jack roared like a lion.

THURSDAY • Phonics, Spelling, and Word Skills

1. **Answer the riddles with words that use _y_ to make the long e sound.**

   a) I have long ears and I hop.   ____ ____ ____ ____ y

   b) You often say this word before "birthday."   ____ ____ ____ ____ y

2. **Remember to use the letters _e_ and _y_ at the end of these words:**
   hockey, money. **Use the clue to write the correct word.**

   a) You play this on ice. _____

   b) You might have this in your pocket. _____

3. **Circle the words made from a prefix and a base word.**

   under   undo   uncover   unlucky

Canadian Daily Language Skills, Grade 2   © Chalkboard Publishing Inc.

FRIDAY • Writing Prompt

Create a poster encouraging people to reduce, reuse, and recycle.

☐ **My writing makes sense.**
☐ **I used capital letters where needed.**
☐ **I put the correct mark at the end of each sentence.**
☐ **My picture is neat and colourful.**

MONDAY • Sentences and Punctuation

1. Use the best word (_so_ or _because_) to join the two sentences.

Put a comma before _so_. Do not put a comma before _because_.

My bedroom looks neat. I cleaned it up.

_____

2. Fill in the circle if the words make a complete sentence.

a) ◯ A squirrel with a bushy tail.

b) ◯ Trees grow slowly.

3. Write the sentence. Add quotation marks.

It is great to see you, said Max.

TUESDAY • Grammar and Usage

1. Write the plural of each noun.

a) shelf: _____   **b)** person: _____

2. Circle the correct word in brackets.

Beth said that this pen is (her's hers), so I will give it back to her.

3. When does the action happen—in the past, present, or future? Circle the answer.

a) We will ride our bikes to the park.   **past   present   future**

b) The bees make honey in their beehive. **past   present   future**

WEDNESDAY • Vocabulary and Figurative Language

1. Finish the simile. Write the word that makes sense.

tomato   mouse   rainbow

The rose was as red as a _____ .

2. Find the mystery word that answers <u>both</u> riddles.
• I am a tiny bit of time.
• I am not first, but I come next.

Mystery word: s ____ ____ ____ ____ d

3. Write the sentence. Use the antonym of the bold word.

None of the children wore mittens.

_____

THURSDAY • Phonics, Spelling, and Word Skills

1. Answer the riddles. Use words that start with the letters *squ*.

a) I am a shape with four corners.   s q u ____ ____ ____

b) Doors need oil when they make this sound.   s q u ____ ____ ____

c) Don't step on a bug or you will do this to it.   s q u ____ ____ ____

2. Choose <u>one</u> of the words below to make <u>two</u> compound words.

ring   wood   cup   bake

a) _____ board   **b)** _____ cake

3. Circle the words made from a prefix and a base word.

return   reach   replay   rerun

FRIDAY • Writing Prompt

A diamante poem is in the shape of a diamond.
Write your own diamante poem using the format below.

Topic _____

_____
(noun)

_____   _____
(adjective)   (adjective)

_____ _____ _____
("ing" verb)   ("ing" verb)   ("ing" verb)

_____   _____
(adjective)   (adjective)

_____
(noun)

MONDAY • Sentences and Punctuation

1. You can use _so_ or _because_ to join two sentences.

   Put a comma before _so_. Do not put a comma before _because_.
   Choose the best word (_so_ or _because_) to join the sentences.

   I want to learn to play piano. I practise every day.

   _____

2. **When you write a date, use a comma after the day of the week and the number of the day.**   _Monday, August 10, 2020_

   Write the date of your birthday.

   _____

TUESDAY • Grammar and Usage

1. **An <u>adjective</u> describes a noun. An <u>adverb</u> can describe a verb.**

   An adverb can tell <u>where</u> an action happens.
   Circle the adjective. Underline the adverb.

   The milk spilled everywhere on the clean floor.

2. **Write the correct verb.**

   I _____ two tickets, and she _____ one ticket.
       has   have   has   have

3. **Circle the correct word.**

   The fire went out by (itself himself).

WEDNESDAY • Vocabulary and Figurative Language

1. **_Flour_ is a white powder for baking.** *We need <u>flour</u> to make a cake.*
   A _flower_ grows on a plant. *Look at the pretty pink <u>flower</u> in the garden.*

   Write the correct word—*flour* or *flower*.

   a) The bee landed on a bright red _____.

   b) Dad got some _____, so we can make muffins.

2. **What do you think the underlined phrase means?**

   No way! I will eat chocolate-covered ants <u>when pigs fly</u>!

   _____

THURSDAY • Phonics, Spelling, and Word Skills

1. **Write a word that has three syllables.** _____

2. **Choose the correct word.**

   a) I would like _____ cookies, please.
   two   to   too

   b) Can I come to the park _____ ?
   two   to   too

3. **Each bold word is missing the same two vowels. Write the vowels.**

   a) Please **w**___ ___ **t** for your turn.

   b) Let's **p** ___ ___ **nt** the walls light blue.

FRIDAY • Writing Prompt

What are you proud of? Draw a picture.

I am proud of _____. Let me tell you why.

First of all, _____

_____

Another reason is _____

_____

Finally, _____

_____

This is why I am proud of _____!

☐ **My writing makes sense.**
☐ **I used capital letters where needed.**
☐ **I put the correct mark at the end of each sentence.**
☐ **My picture is neat and colourful**

MONDAY • Sentences and Punctuation

1. Put the correct punctuation mark at the end of each sentence.

a) Are you going to join the club____

b) Set the table for dinner____

2. Fill in the circle if the words make a complete sentence.

a) ◯ In the morning.

b) ◯ I see a bird in the tree.

3. Write the sentence. Correct the mistakes.

we won the soccer championships "shouted Andrew"

_____

TUESDAY • Grammar and Usage

1. An adverb can describe a verb.

Underline the adverb that tells <u>when</u> something is happening in the sentence.

Tomorrow my class is going on a field trip.

2. Write the correct verb.

Next year I _____ a year older.
was   am   will be

3. Write the correct word.

I can't wait _____ recess.
until   on   in

WEDNESDAY • Vocabulary and Figurative Language

1. **Someone who stays up late is called a "night owl."**
   My sister never goes to bed early. She is a night owl.

   Are you a "night owl?" Tell why or why not.

   _____

   _____

2. **Find the mystery word that answers <u>both</u> riddles.**
   • I am small and have two wings.
   • I am what kites and airplanes do.   **Mystery word:** ____ ____ ____

3. **Circle the antonym for the bold word.**

   I will **receive** an award at the assembly.   **make   give   see**

THURSDAY • Phonics, Spelling, and Word Skills

1. **Answer the riddles with words that have the long *o* sound.**

   a) You have many in your body.   b ____ ____ ____ ____

   b) Kings and queens sit on them.   t h r ____ ____ ____ ____

2. **For each word, underline the base word and circle the prefix.**

   a) rebuild   **b)** preschool   **c)** unlock

3. **Remember to write a *d* before the *g* in these words—*fridge, judge*.**
   Use the clue to write the word.

   a) I sit in a courtoom.   _____

   b) Food is put in me to keep cold.   _____

FRIDAY • Writing Prompt

Complete the advertisment to convince people to buy a bike.

Buy this _____ bike!

Description

_____

_____

_____

_____

Selling Price _____ **Contact Number** _____

☐ My writing makes sense.
☐ I used capital letters where needed.
☐ I put the correct mark at the end of each sentence.

MONDAY • Sentences and Punctuation

1. Put the correct punctuation mark at the end of each sentence.

a) Would you like a snack___   **b)** This is the best day ever___

2. Add commas to the list in each sentence.

a) The sports store sells bikes helmets nets and balls.

b) Harry Prya and Mara are in my class.

3. Write the sentence. Correct the mistakes.

What is for dinner!" said Dad·

_____

TUESDAY • Grammar and Usage

1. Circle the nouns. Underline the verb.

I saw a white bunny and yellow chick at the farm.

2. Circle the correct word in brackets.

I see a boy. The (boys   boy's   boys') coach is talking to him.

3. Complete the sentence.

This year's concert is _____ than last year's concert.
                       long   longer   longest

4. Circle the correct word.

Sara and Lee, please help (themselves   yourselves) to another drink.

WEDNESDAY • Vocabulary and Figurative Language

1. Circle the onomatopoeic words in the sentence.

The car zoomed around the corner and beeped at the people.

2. Circle the meaning of the bold word in the sentence.

I know I need to rest when my body feels **weary**.

cold   hungry   tired

3. Write the sentence. Use the antonym of the bold word.

Everybody wants to play tag today.

_____

THURSDAY • Phonics, Spelling, and Word Skills

1. Answer the riddles with words that use *y* to make the long *e* sound.

a) I am a baby dog.   ____ ____ ____ ____ y

b) This is how I feel when I need to eat.   ____ ____ ____ ____ ____ y

2. Choose the correct word.

_____ are four people in each group.
   There   Their

3. Write a word that rhymes with the bold word.

a) boat _____   **b) show** _____

FRIDAY • Writing Prompt

What would it be like to have 100 pets? Draw and write about it.

_____

_____

_____

_____

_____

☐ **My writing makes sense.**
☐ **I used capital letters where needed.**
☐ **I put the correct mark at the end of each sentence.**
☐ **My picture is neat and colourful.**

MONDAY • Sentences and Punctuation

1. Use the best word (_so_ or _because**_) to join the two sentences.**

Put a comma before _so_. Do not put a comma before _because**_.**

I was tired. I went to sleep.

_____

2. Fill in the circle if the words make a complete sentence.

a) ◯ All the children.   **b)** ◯ The sun is bright.

3. Write the sentence. Add quotation marks.

Let's go to the playground, said Millie.

_____

TUESDAY • Grammar and Usage

1. Write the plural of each noun.

a) hand: _____   **b)** toe: _____

2. Write _I_ or _me_ to complete the sentence.

Jason and _____ are in the school show.

3. When does the action happen—in the past, present, or future? Circle the answer.

a) We baked cookies last night.   **past   present   future**

b) They will leave after school for the game.   **past   present   future**

WEDNESDAY • Vocabulary and Figurative Language

1. Finish the simile. Write a word or phrase that makes sense.

Harry was as loud as _____.

2. Circle the meaning of the bold word in the sentence.

Lisa looked for her bag, but she could not **locate** it.

> find   lose   pick up

3. Find the mystery word that answers <u>both</u> riddles.
   • I am something people do with a car.
   • I am a place with trees and grass.

Mystery word: p ____ ____ ____

THURSDAY • Phonics, Spelling, and Word Skills

1. Write <u>two</u> words that rhyme with the bold word.

lake _____

2. Make <u>two</u> compound words using the words below.

flower   basket   sun   ball

_____

3. Circle the words that have a silent e.

make   elephant   rope   shake

FRIDAY • Writing Prompt

Here is some advice. *Children should eat fruits and vegetables every day.*
Draw a picture.

I (agree   disagree) with this advice. Let me tell you why.

First of all, _____

_____

Another reason is _____

_____

Finally, _____

_____

This is why I (agree   disagree) with this advice.

- ☐ **My writing makes sense.**
- ☐ **I used capital letters where needed.**
- ☐ **I put the correct mark at the end of each sentence.**
- ☐ **My picture is neat and colourful.**

MONDAY • Sentences and Punctuation

1. What kind of sentence is it? Circle the answer.

a) Tie your shoelaces.   **exclamation   command   statement**

b) I like basketball.   **statement   command   question**

c) Go away!   **question   statement   exclamation**

2. Add words to make a complete sentence.

The race cars _____.

3. Write a sentence where someone is talking.

_____

TUESDAY • Grammar and Usage

1. Write a sentence that includes an adjective and adverb.

_____

2. Write the correct word.

I think vanilla ice cream tastes _____ than strawberry.

                                       better   best

3. Circle the correct word in brackets.   (Ours Our) family has three pets.

4. Write the correct word.

The _____ clothing department is on the first floor.

       women's   womens

WEDNESDAY • Vocabulary and Figurative Language

1. Circle the onomatopoeic words in the sentence.

   a) The fire crackled and snapped in the fireplace.

   b) The key jingles in the pocket of his coat.

2. Circle the synonym for the bold word.

   Mom **searched** everywhere for her car keys. **looked**   **watched**   **saw**

3. Finish the simile. Write the word that makes sense.

   glove   **cloud**   **book**

   These pants are just the right size. They fit like a _____.

THURSDAY • Phonics, Spelling, and Word Skills

1. Answer the riddles with words that use *ow* to make the *oo* sound.

   a) I like to swim in this on a hot day.   ____ o o ____

   b) I read this to learn about things.   ____ o o ____

2. Make <u>three</u> compound words using the words below.

   set   castle   sun   sand   shine

   _____   _____   _____

3. Write two more words in the same word family as the bold word.

   night: light _____

FRIDAY • Writing Prompt

An acrostic poem is a poem in which the first letters of each line spell out a word or phrase.

Choose a topic and write an acrostic poem.
Print the topic name (vertically) down the left side.

___ _____

___ _____

___ _____

___ _____

___ _____

___ _____

___ _____

___ _____

☐ **My writing makes sense.**
☐ **I used capital letters where needed.**
☐ **I put the correct mark at the end of each sentence.**

Title _____

_____

_____

_____

_____

_____

_____

☐ **My writing makes sense.**
☐ **I used capital letters where needed.**
☐ **I put the correct mark at the end of each sentence.**
☐ **My picture is neat and colourful.**

Canadian Daily Language Skills, Grade 2   © Chalkboard Publishing Inc.

How to _____

First, _____

_____

_____

Next, _____

_____

_____

Then, _____

_____

_____

Finally, _____

_____

Adjectives for Writing

Category	Adjectives
Size	big, small, short, tall, fat, skinny, large, medium, slim, thin, slender, tiny, lean, scrawny, huge, gigantic, jumbo, plump, wee, wide, narrow
Shape	round, square, pointed, jagged, oval, chunky, curly, straight, curved, flat, twisted, heart-shaped, spiky, wavy, bent, tangled, messy
Colour	red, orange, yellow, green, blue, purple, pink, grey, white, black, brown, silver, gold
Age	young, old, new, baby, newborn
Sound	loud, quiet, long, short, musical, surprising, soft, noisy, muffled, whispering, growling, grumbling
Light and Brightness	dull, bright, dark, light, clear, flashy, flashing, dim, faint, glowing, flickering, twinkly, twinkling, shiny, shining
Smell	good, bad, strong, sweet, salty, spicy, stinky, sour, delicious, yummy, fresh, rotten, rotting
Feel and Texture	soft, hard, smooth, rough, silky, fluffy, fuzzy, furry, wet, dry, bumpy, lumpy, scratchy, sweaty, slippery, slimy, gritty, dirty, sticky, gummy, jiggly, wiggly, squishy, watery, liquid, solid, rock hard, damp, stiff, firm
Taste	delicious, bitter, sweet, salty, tasty, spicy, yummy, bland, sour, strong
Speed and Movement	quick, quickly, fast, slow, slowly, rapid, rapidly, brisk, briskly, swift, swiftly, instant, instantly, late
Temperature	hot, cold, icy, frosty, chilly, burning, boiling, steamy, sizzling, cool, warm, freezing, frozen, damp, humid, melting

How Am I Doing?

	Completing my work	Using my time wisely	Following directions	Keeping organized
Full speed ahead!	• My work is always complete and done with care. • I added extra details to my work.	• I always get my work done on time.	• I always follow directions.	• My materials are always neatly organized. • I am always prepared and ready to learn.
Keep going!	• My work is complete and done with care. • I added extra details to my work.	• I usually get my work done on time.	• I usually follow directions without reminders.	• I usually can find my materials. • I am usually prepared and ready to learn.
Slow down!	• My work is complete. • I need to check my work.	• I sometimes get my work done on time.	• I sometimes need reminders to follow directions.	• I sometimes need time to find my materials. • I am sometimes prepared and ready to learn.
Stop!	• My work is not complete. • I need to check my work.	• I rarely get my work done on time.	• I need reminders to follow directions.	• I need to organize my materials. • I am rarely prepared and ready to learn.

_____'s *Completion Chart*

Colour each week you complete.

Week		Week	
1	☆ ☆ ☆ ☆ ☆	19	☆ ☆ ☆ ☆ ☆
2	☆ ☆ ☆ ☆ ☆	20	☆ ☆ ☆ ☆ ☆
3	☆ ☆ ☆ ☆ ☆	21	☆ ☆ ☆ ☆ ☆
4	☆ ☆ ☆ ☆ ☆	22	☆ ☆ ☆ ☆ ☆
5	☆ ☆ ☆ ☆ ☆	23	☆ ☆ ☆ ☆ ☆
6	☆ ☆ ☆ ☆ ☆	24	☆ ☆ ☆ ☆ ☆
7	☆ ☆ ☆ ☆ ☆	25	☆ ☆ ☆ ☆ ☆
8	☆ ☆ ☆ ☆ ☆	26	☆ ☆ ☆ ☆ ☆
9	☆ ☆ ☆ ☆ ☆	27	☆ ☆ ☆ ☆ ☆
10	☆ ☆ ☆ ☆ ☆	28	☆ ☆ ☆ ☆ ☆
11	☆ ☆ ☆ ☆ ☆	29	☆ ☆ ☆ ☆ ☆
12	☆ ☆ ☆ ☆ ☆	30	☆ ☆ ☆ ☆ ☆
13	☆ ☆ ☆ ☆ ☆	31	☆ ☆ ☆ ☆ ☆
14	☆ ☆ ☆ ☆ ☆	32	☆ ☆ ☆ ☆ ☆
15	☆ ☆ ☆ ☆ ☆	33	☆ ☆ ☆ ☆ ☆
16	☆ ☆ ☆ ☆ ☆	34	☆ ☆ ☆ ☆ ☆
17	☆ ☆ ☆ ☆ ☆	35	☆ ☆ ☆ ☆ ☆
18	☆ ☆ ☆ ☆ ☆		

Canadian Daily Language Skills, Grade 2   © Chalkboard Publishing Inc.

Fantastic Work!

Canadian Daily Language Skills, Grade 2

Answers to Exercises

WEEK 1, pp. 3–5

Monday 1. Fill in b) 2. a) A toad b) Clouds 3. The sky is full of stars.

Tuesday 1. people: mother, John, doctor; places: town, school; things: bike, toy, table
2. longer 3. a) cats b) books c) games

Wednesday 1. whole 2. begin 3. ring

Thursday 1. skate 2. a) isn't b) can't c) won't
3. sunset, spaceship

Friday Check that the items in the checklist at the bottom of the exercise are covered.

WEEK 2, pp. 6–8

Monday 1. Fill in a) and b) 2. a) period
b) question mark 3. a) exclamation mark b) period
OR exclamation mark

Tuesday 1. a) old b) green c) loud 2. play 3. until

Wednesday 1. ice 2. dirty 3. give back

Thursday 1. month 2. step, big 3. a) watch b) play
c) swim d) tall

Friday Check that the items in the checklist at the bottom of the exercise are covered.

WEEK 3, pp. 9–11

Monday 1. Fill in b) 2. My uncle 3. I waved at Sam, and he waved at me. 4. a) question mark
b) exclamation mark

Tuesday 1. a) past b) present 2. Nick's
3. a) classes b) foxes c) lunches d) dishes

Wednesday 1. Answers will vary. You might wish to ask a few students to share with the class. 2. loud

Thursday 1. a) tail b) drain 2. jump 3. a) she's
b) they're c) I'm

Friday Check that the items in the checklist at the bottom of the exercise are covered..

WEEK 4, pp. 12–14

Monday 1. Fill in b) 2. A blue butterfly 3. I made a snack, and I shared it with Tim. 4. a) period b) period
OR exclamation mark

Tuesday 1. Check that the proper nouns are capitalized. 2. She

Wednesday 1. tack 2. a thought 3. last

Thursday 1. a) whale b) wheel 2. funny, under
3. sometimes, inside

Friday Check for correct spelling and punctuation, and for capital letters where needed.

WEEK 5, pp. 15–17

Monday 1. Sample answers: purred in my lap; purrs when I pat it; is very soft 2. a) The baseball player
b) A strong wind 3. a) exclamation mark b) question mark

Tuesday 1. a) playful, yellow b) tiny, red 2. tallest
3. after

Wednesday 1. their 2. angry 3. tie

Thursday 1. play 2. Fill in a) 3. Sample answers: train, plain, main, gain, pain, stain

Friday Check that the description is clear, and that the child uses correct punctuation and capital letters where needed.

WEEK 6, pp. 18–20

Monday 1. a) hop across the grass b) barks at cats
2. Sami, David, and Julie went fishing last weekend.

Tuesday 1. reads, listen 2. present 3. Peter's

Wednesday 1. elephant 2. quiet 3. get ready

Thursday 1. black 2. over, into 3. a) tie b) do
c) correct d) happy

Friday Check that the items in the checklist at the bottom of the exercise are covered.

WEEK 7, pp. 21–23

Monday 1. a) is very bumpy b) play soccer
2. Sara wants to draw, but I want to paint. OR Sara wants to draw, and I want to paint. 3. a) question mark b) exclamation mark

Tuesday 1. They 2. a) an b) a c) a d) an
3. yourselves

Wednesday 1. Answers will vary. You may wish to ask a few children to share with the class. 2. pretty 3. take off

Thursday 1. feet 2. Fill in b) 3. raincoat, sidewalk

Friday Check that the items in the checklist at the bottom of the exercise are covered.

WEEK 8, pp. 24–26

Monday 1. a) burns brightly b) are laughing
2. Zebras have stripes, and they can run fast.
3. a) period b) period OR exclamation mark

Tuesday 1. circle: soup, doctor, sandbox; underline: underline: speak, hop, stir 2. a) mice b) people c) children d) women 3. him

Wednesday 1. fish 2. letters 3. middle

Thursday 1. chair 2. tiger, robin 3. Fill in a)
4. a) he'll b) they'll c) I'll

Friday Check that the description is clear and that the child uses correct punctuation and capital letters where needed.

WEEK 9, pp. 27–29

Monday 1. a) question mark b) period 2. is my brother's teacher 3. I want to run, but my foot hurts.
4. I need a pencil, eraser, and paper to do my work.

Tuesday 1. white, soft 2. faster 3. a) present b) future

Wednesday 1. tale 2. afraid 3. say again

Thursday 1. a) read b) leaf c) steam 2. Fill in b)

Friday Check for spelling, capital letters where needed, and that the poem follows the diamante format of nouns, adjectives, verbs, adjectives, nouns.

WEEK 10, pp. 30–32

Monday 1. a) period b) question mark 2. The boy and girl sing a song. 3. Karen and I love riddles.

Tuesday 1. They 2. fly, goes 3. mine

Wednesday 1. rock 2. opened 3. save from danger

Thursday 1. a) March b) branch 2. I have two pieces of gum. 3. John made three wishes.

Friday Check that the items in the checklist at the bottom of the exercise are covered.

WEEK 11, pp. 33–35

Monday 1. a) exclamation mark b) period 2. My green socks 3. The flowers are pretty, and they smell nice.

Tuesday 1. a) bushes b) peaches c) ears
2. a) future b) present 3. furry, red

Wednesday 1. Answers will vary. You may wish to have a few children share with the class. 2. tidy 3. waves

Thursday 1. bite 2. a) walking b) reading
3. Sample answers: bin, kin, tin, win, spin, skin

Friday Check that the steps follow a logical order and are written clearly.

WEEK 12, pp. 36–38

Monday 1. a) period b) exclamation mark 2. Check that there is a comma after the day of the week and the number of the day. 3. Check that the sentence ends with an exclamation mark.

Tuesday **1.** circle: road, mountain, dog; underline: write, think, dig **2.** like, has **3.** by

Wednesday **1.** snow **2.** light **3.** smile

Thursday **1.** thirsty **2.** into, maybe **3.** a) piece b) friend

Friday Check that the items in the checklist at the bottom of the exercise are covered.

WEEK 13, pp. 39–41

Monday **1.** Sample answers: I saw elephants; We saw lots of animals; We had a great time **2.** a) Rain b) Two little mice **3.** Jeff and Kim eat grapes.

Tuesday **1.** quietly **2.** biggest **3.** a) yours b) us

Wednesday **1.** buy, by **2.** spot **3.** go into

Thursday **1.** a) sky b) cry c) July **2.** watched

Friday Check that the items in the checklist at the bottom of the exercise are covered.

WEEK 14, pp. 42–44

Monday **1.** Sample answers: There are fluffy clouds; I see birds flying; Planes fly **2.** rolls across the floor **3.** I thought I lost my pen, but I found it. **4.** When is Leo's birthday?

Tuesday **1.** a) keys b) babies c) boxes **2.** saw **3.** funny, green **4.** themselves

Wednesday **1.** Answers will vary. You may wish to have a few children share with the class. **2.** It rained all night. **3.** pink

Thursday **1.** a) shade b) shower c) shark **2.** family, hospital, elephant **3.** a) speak b) fill

Friday Check that the items in the checklist at the bottom of the exercise are covered.

WEEK 15, pp. 45–47

Monday **1.** a) period b) question mark **2.** The dog barked, and jumped up. **3.** hangs in that web

4. Check that there is a comma after the day of the week and the number of the day.

Tuesday **1.** happily **2.** are, is **3.** Wendy's

Wednesday **1.** Answers will vary. You may wish to ask a few children to share with the class. **2.** sad **3.** very quiet

Thursday **1.** a) pilot b) iron **2.** Fill in b) **3.** everyone, Sunday

Friday Check for complete sentences, capital letters where needed, and periods at the end of sentences.

WEEK 16, pp. 48–50

Monday **1.** a) question mark b) period **2.** underline: is in the park; circle: The carousel **3.** Everyone might leave, but some people might stay.

Tuesday **1.** a) circle: straw, cloud, zoo; underline: hide, eat, bake b) circle: pillow, ant, desk; underline: say, take, think. **2.** will go **3.** from

Wednesday **1.** eagle **2.** watch **3.** She forgets to close the window.

Thursday **1.** a) smell b) smile **2.** a) rain|bow b) in|to c) un|der **3.** a) ready b) early

Friday Check that the child's name is spelled properly and can be read vertically.

WEEK 17, pp. 51–53

Monday **1.** a) exclamation mark b) period **2.** Some sharks are big, and have sharp teeth. **3.** When are you moving in June?

Tuesday **1.** heavier **2.** mice, feet, men **3.** himself **4.** circle: man, hammer, bench; underline: takes

Wednesday **1.** Answers will vary. You may wish to have a few children share with the class. **2.** sizzled **3.** bark

Thursday **1.** high **2.** Fill in a) **3.** Are you going to the party?

Friday Check for complete sentences, capital letters where needed, and periods at the end of sentences.

WEEK 18, pp. 54–56

Monday **1.** period **2.** underline: scares the children; circle: Loud thunder **3.** Giraffes have long legs, and they can run fast.

Tuesday **1.** sing, sings **2.** a) ours b) his **3.** children's

Wednesday **1.** diamonds **2.** Today, we have more homework. **3.** a little bit wet

Thursday **1.** a) push b) brush **2.** a) win|ter b) num|ber c) Mon|day **3.** a) sunflower b) sandbox

Friday Check that the postcard is addressed and signed properly, and that the child uses complete sentences, capital letters where needed, and periods at the end of sentences.

WEEK 19, pp. 57–59

Monday **1.** a) question mark b) period **2.** Fill in a) and b) **3.** A red bird and a big dog are in the photo.

Tuesday **1.** gently **2.** am **3.** into

Wednesday **1.** Answers will vary. You may wish to ask a few children to share with the class. **2.** our

Thursday **1.** a) cone b) smoke **2.** a) underline: make; circle: re b) underline: appear; circle: dis c) underline: tie; circle: un **3.** a) bridge b) fudge

Friday Check that the steps follow a logical order and are written clearly.

WEEK 20, pp. 60–62

Monday **1.** a) question b) exclamation **2.** I could watch a movie, but it is almost my bedtime. **3.** underline: rolled all the way down the hill; circle: The boys

Tuesday **1.** a) a b) an c) an d) a **2.** worse **3.** a) ourselves b) themselves

Wednesday **1.** pancake **2.** cow **3.** easy

Thursday **1.** a) phone b) alphabet **2.** a) farmer b) singer

Friday Check for spelling, capital letters where needed, and that the poem follows the diamante format of nouns, adjectives, verbs, adjectives, nouns.

WEEK 21, pp. 63–65

Monday **1.** a) period b) exclamation mark **2.** An airplane has wings and can fly far. **3.** Will you help Frida do her homework?

Tuesday **1.** a) cities b) monkeys **2.** smiles, see **3.** a) his b) their

Wednesday **1.** write, right **2.** make afraid

Thursday **1.** a) road b) boat **2.** a) fingernail b) raindrop **3.** Sample answers: look, took, rook, cook, nook, crook, brook

Friday Check that the items in the checklist at the bottom of the exercise are covered.

WEEK 22, pp. 66–68

Monday **1.** Jim is very tired, so he will sleep well tonight. **2.** I like baseball, hockey, soccer, and swimming. **3.** Can some snakes swim?

Tuesday **1.** a) circle: new; underline: softly b) circle: silly; underline: loudly **2.** went **3.** at

Wednesday **1.** giraffe **2.** when the sun comes up **3.** under

Thursday **1.** a) pitch b) watch c) scratch **2.** a) per|fect b) back|pack c) sad|ness **3.** Fill in b)

Friday Check that the items in the checklist at the bottom of the exercise are covered.

WEEK 23, pp. 69–71

Monday **1.** a) statement b) command c) exclamation **2.** Sample answers: are a lot alike; like the same things; have been friends for years; live next door to each other **3.** Answers will vary. Check that the items in the list are separated by commas.

Tuesday   1. circle: elephants, water, pond; underline: drink   **2.** best   **3.** girls'   **4.** herself

Wednesday   1. Answers will vary. You may wish to ask a few children to share with the class.   **2.** almost   **3.** lie

Thursday   1. a) snow b) bowl   **2.** Fill in a)
3. Sample answers: law, caw, raw, draw, claw, gnaw, craw

Friday   Check that the items in the checklist at the bottom of the exercise are covered.

WEEK 24, pp. 72–74

Monday   1. a) period b) exclamation mark   **2.** People made cakes, cookies, and muffins for the bake sale.   **3.** played in the treetops   **4.** question

Tuesday   1. a) leaves b) teeth   **2.** theirs   **3.** with   **4.** will be

Wednesday   1. glass   **2.** make someone remember   **3.** a) lamb OR sheep b) duck

Thursday   1. a) badge b) fudge c) hedge
2. a) Sep|tem|ber b) ham|burg|er   **3.** a) without b) outside

Friday   Check that the items in the checklist at the bottom of the exercise are covered.

WEEK 25, pp. 75–77

Monday   1. I need to do my homework because it is almost bedtime..   **2.** a) We got gum, suckers, apples, and chocolate bars on Halloween. b) I have yellow, red, orange, and blue pencils in my knapsack.

Tuesday   1. circle: busy; underline: safely   **2.** has, have   **3.** himself

Wednesday   1. pear   **2.** huge   **3.** talk about

Thursday   1. a) huge b) rules   **2.** Fill in a)

Friday   Check for complete sentences, capital letters where needed, and periods at the end of sentences.

WEEK 26, pp. 78–80

Monday   1. a) period b) question mark   **2.** Fill in a)
3. The snow is melting and it will be gone soon. OR The snow is melting and will be gone soon.

Tuesday   1. circle: children, park; underline: run, play   **2.** worst   **3.** a) am b) played

Wednesday   1. feather   **2.** a) clock b) dog   **3.** get away

Thursday   1. scratch   **2.** a) wa|ter|fall b) bar|be|cue   **3.** greener

Friday   Check that the items in the checklist at the bottom of the exercise are covered.

WEEK 27, pp. 81–83

Monday   1. a) statement b) question c) command and exclamation   **2.** a) "We will have fun," said Tara. b) "I like when it snows," said Lewis.

Tuesday   1. people, women, songs   **2.** a) Tammy's b) animals'   **3.** a) me b) I   **4.** Answers will vary. You may wish to ask a few children to share with the class.

Wednesday   1. Answers will vary. You may wish to ask a few children to share with the class.   **2.** hurry   **3.** rock

Thursday   1. a) new b) chew c) screw
2. a) toothpaste b) toothbrush   **3.** recount, rename

Friday   Check that the items in the checklist at the bottom of the exercise are covered.

WEEK 28, pp. 84–86

Monday   1. underline: played lacrosse in the park; circle: Sandy and Tasneem   **2.** a) Carlos asked, "May I play, too?" b) Mia asked, "Are you in grade two?"   **3.** The school is big and has lots of windows.

Tuesday   1. circle: huge; underline: bravely   **2.** are, am   **3.** after

Wednesday   1. night   **2.** I had a nap after the soccer game.   **3.** eat in small bites

Canadian Daily Language Skills, Grade 2   © Chalkboard Publishing Inc.

Thursday **1.** a) spring b) spread **2.** a) cover b) write
3. sweetest

Friday Check that the items in the checklist at the
bottom of the exercise are covered.

WEEK 29, pp. 87–89

Monday **1.** a) period b) question mark **2.** a) The pet
store sells kittens, puppies, fish, and hamsters.
b) Birds, raccoons, and foxes live in the forest.
2. "What a nice surprise!" said Mom.

Tuesday **1.** circle: bus, truck, road; underline: drive
2. tinier **3.** will be **4.** itself

Wednesday **1.** present **2.** shake **3.** Fill in a)

Thursday **1.** a) bunny b) happy **2.** a) hockey
b) money **3.** undo, uncover, unlucky

Friday Check that the poster's message is clear and
that the child uses correct punctuation and capital
letters where needed.

WEEK 30, pp. 90–92

Monday **1.** My bedroom looks neat because I
cleaned it up. **2.** Fill in b) **3.** "It is great to see you,"
said Max.

Tuesday **1.** a) shelves b) people **2.** hers
3. a) future b) present

Wednesday **1.** tomato **2.** second **3.** All of the
children wore mittens.

Thursday **1.** a) square b) squeak c) squish OR
squash **2.** a) cupboard b) cupcake **3.** return, replay,
rerun

Friday Check for spelling, capital letters where
needed, and that the poem follows the diamante
format of nouns, adjectives, verbs, adjectives, nouns.

WEEK 31, pp. 93–95

Monday **1.** I want to learn to play piano, so I practise
every day. **2.** Check that there is a comma after the
day of the week and the number of the day.

Tuesday **1.** circle: clean; underline: everywhere
2. have, has **3.** itself

Wednesday **1.** a) flower b) flour **2.** Answers will
vary. You may wish to have a few children share with
the class.

Thursday **1.** Answers will vary. Check that the word
has the correct number of syllables. **2.** a) two b) too
3. a) ai, wait b) ai, paint

Friday Check that the items in the checklist at the
bottom of the exercise are covered.

WEEK 32, pp. 96–98

Monday **1.** a) question mark b) period
2. Fill in b) **3.** "We won the soccer championships!"
shouted Andrew.

Tuesday **1.** underline: Tomorrow **2.** will be **3.** until

Wednesday **1.** Answers will vary. You may wish to
ask a few children to share with the class. **2.** fly
3. give

Thursday **1.** a) bones b) thrones **2.** a) underline:
build; circle: re b) underline: school; circle: pre
c) underline: lock; circle: un **3.** a) judge b) fridge

Friday Check that the items in the checklist at the
bottom of the exercise are covered.

WEEK 33, pp. 99–101

Monday **1.** a) question mark b) exclamation mark
2. a) The sports store sells bikes, helmets, nets, and
balls. b) Harry, Prya, and Mara are in my class.
3. "What is for dinner?" said Dad.

Tuesday **1.** circle: bunny, chick, farm; underline: saw
2. boy's **3.** longer **4.** yourselves

Wednesday **1.** zoomed, beeped **2.** tired
3. Nobody wants to play tag today.

Thursday **1.** a) puppy b) hungry **2.** There
3. a) Sample answers: coat, goat, moat, gloat, float,
note b) Sample answers: glow, flow, row, mow, throw

Friday Check that the items in the checklist at the
bottom of the exercise are covered.

Monday   **1.** I was tired, so I went to sleep.   **2.** Fill in b)   **3.** "Let's go to the playground," said Millie.

Tuesday   **1.** a) hands b) toes   **2.** I   **3.** a) past b) future

Wednesday   **1.** Answers will vary. You may wish to ask a few children to share with the class.   **2.** find **3.** park

Thursday   **1.** Sample answers: bake, cake, shake, make, take   **2.** sunflower, basketball   **3.** make, rope, shape

Friday   Check that the items in the checklist at the bottom of the exercise are covered.

Monday   **1.** a) command b) statement c) exclamation AND command   **2.** Sample answers: zoomed around the track; were all red; made a lot of noise   **3.** Answers will vary. Check that the sentence includes quotation marks.

Tuesday   **1.** Answers will vary.   **2.** better   **3.** Our **4.** women's

Wednesday   **1.** a) crackled, snapped b) jingles **2.** looked   **3.** glove

Thursday   **1.** a) pool b) book   **2.** sunset, sandcastle, sunshine   **3.** Sample answers: right, sight, bright, fight, might, tight

Friday   Check that the child's name is spelled properly and can be read vertically.